easter source

A comprehensive seasonal collection

We hope you enjoy *Easter Source*. Further copies are available
from your local Kevin Mayhew stockist.

In case of difficulty, or to request a catalogue,
please contact the publisher direct by writing to:

The Sales Department
KEVIN MAYHEW LTD
Buxhall
Stowmarket
Suffolk IP14 3BW

Phone 01449 737978
Fax 01449 737834
E-mail info@kevinmayhewltd.com

First published in Great Britain in 2003 by Kevin Mayhew Ltd.

© Copyright 2003 Kevin Mayhew Ltd.

ISBN 1 84417 030 6
ISMN M 57024 169 9
Catalogue No: 1470140

0 1 2 3 4 5 6 7 8 9

Cover design by Angela Selfe

Printed and bound in Great Britain

Easter Source is the definitive collection of hymns and songs for the season of Lent and Easter.

Alongside well-loved traditional hymns is a selection of related worship songs and children's songs.

Users will find this superbly produced volume an invaluable resource with a rich variety of styles and a unique blend of old and new.

1 Above the clash of creeds
(No other way)

Words and Music: Graham Kendrick

1. A-bove the clash of creeds, the ma-ny voi-ces

that call on so ma-ny names,

in-to these fi – nal days our God has spo – ken

by send – ing his on – ly Son.

Chorus

There is no o - ther way by which we must be saved; his name is Je - sus, the on - ly Sa - viour; no o - ther sin - less life, no o - ther sac - ri - fice, in all cre - a - tion no o - ther way.

2. Before we called he came
   to earth from heaven,
   our maker became a man;
   when no one else could pay,
   he bought our freedom,
   exchanging his life for ours.

3. Beneath the cross of Christ
   let earth fall silent
   in awe of this mystery;
   then let this song arise
   and fill the nations:
   O hear him call, 'Come to me.'

2 Alas! and did my Saviour bleed

(At the cross)

Words: Isaac Watts and Ralph E. Hudson,
based on Matthew 27: 35-50

Music: Ralph E. Hudson

1. Alas! and did my Saviour bleed and did my Sov-'reign die? Would he de-vote that sa-cred head for sin-ners such as I?

Chorus

At the cross, at the cross where I first saw the light and the bur-den of my heart rolled a-way. It was

there by faith I re-ceived my sight, and now I am hap-py all the day!

2. Was it for crimes that I have done
   he groaned upon the tree?
   Amazing pity! Grace unknown!
   And love beyond degree!

3. But drops of grief can ne'er repay
   the debt of love I owe:
   here, Lord, I give myself away,
   'tis all that I can do!

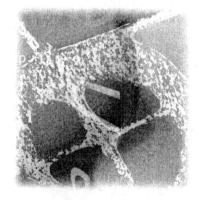

3 Alleluia, alleluia, give thanks to the risen Lord

Words and Music: Donald Fishel, alt.
arr. Andrew Moore

Chorus
Al-le-lu-ia, al-le-lu-ia, give thanks to the ri-sen Lord, al-le-lu-ia, al-le-lu-ia, give praise to his name.

1. Je-sus is Lord of all the earth.
He is the King of cre-a-tion.

2. Spread the good news o'er all the earth.
   Jesus has died and is risen.

3. We have been crucified with Christ.
   Now we shall live for ever.

4. God has proclaimed the just reward:
   'Life for us all, alleluia!'

5. Come, let us praise the living God,
   joyfully sing to our Saviour.

4 Alleluia, alleluia, hearts to heaven and voices raise

Words: Christopher Wordsworth

Music: Arthur Seymour Sullivan

LUX EOI 87 87 D

1. Al - le - lu - ia, al - le - lu - ia, hearts to heav'n and voi - ces raise;

sing to God a hymn of glad - ness, sing to God a hymn of praise:

he who on the cross a vic - tim for the world's sal - va - tion bled,

Je - sus Christ, the King of Glo - ry, now is ri - sen from the dead.

2. Christ is risen, Christ the first-fruits
   of the holy harvest field,
   which will all its full abundance
   at his second coming yield;
   then the golden ears of harvest
   will their heads before him wave,
   ripened by his glorious sunshine,
   from the furrows of the grave.

3. Christ is risen, we are risen;
   shed upon us heavn'ly grace,
   rain, and dew, and gleams of glory
   from the brightness of thy face;
   that we, with our hearts in heaven,
   here on earth may fruitful be,
   and by angel-hands be gathered,
   and be ever, Lord, with thee.

4. Alleluia, alleluia,
   glory be to God on high;
   alleluia to the Saviour,
   who has gained the victory;
   alleluia to the Spirit,
   fount of love and sanctity;
   alleluia, alleluia,
   to the Triune Majesty.

5 Alleluia, alleluia, Jesus, risen Lord of life!

Words and Music: Bernadette Farrell

6 All glory, laud and honour

Words: *Gloria, laus et honor* by St Theodulph
of Orleans trans. John Mason Neale

Music: Melchior Teschner

ST THEODULPH 76 76 and Refrain

Chorus

All glo-ry, laud and hon - our, to thee, Re-deem-er King, to

whom the lips of child - ren made sweet ho-san - nas ring.

1. Thou art the King of Is - rael, thou Da-vid's roy-al Son, who

in the Lord's name com - est, the King and bless-ed one.

2. The company of angels
   are praising thee on high,
   and mortals, joined with all things
   created, make reply.

3. The people of the Hebrews
   with palms before thee went:
   our praise and prayer and anthems
   before thee we present.

4. To thee before thy passion
   they sang their hymns of praise:
   to thee now high exalted
   our melody we raise.

5. Thou didst accept their praises,
   accept the prayers we bring,
   who in all good delightest,
   thou good and gracious king.

7 All heaven declares

Words and Music: Noel and Tricia Richards

Majestically

1. All heav'n de-clares the glo-ry of the ri - sen Lord.

Who can com-pare with the beau-ty of the Lord?

For-e-ver he will be the Lamb up-on the throne.

I glad-ly bow the knee and wor-ship him a - lone.

2. I will proclaim
the glory of the risen Lord.
Who once was slain
to reconcile us to God.
For ever you will be
the Lamb upon the throne.
I gladly bow the knee
and worship you alone.

8 All I once held dear

(Knowing you)

Words and Music: Graham Kendrick

1. All I once held dear, built my life up-on, all this

world re-veres, and wars to own, all I once thought gain I have

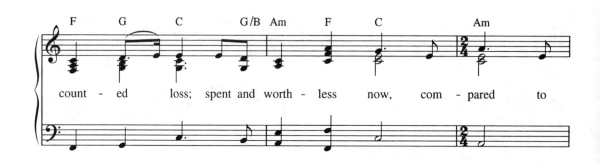

count-ed loss; spent and worth-less now, com-pared to

this. Know-ing you, Je-sus, know-ing you, there

Am   Em/G   F   C/E   F/A

is   no great-er   thing.   You're my all,   you're the best,   you're my

C/G   F   C/E   F/A   C/G   G

To repeat

joy, my right-eous-ness,   and I   love   you,   Lord.   2. Now my

Last time

C/E   F/A   C/G   F/G   C

love   you,   Lord,   love   you,   Lord.

2. Now my heart's desire
   is to know you more,
   to be found in you
   and known as yours.
   To possess by faith
   what I could not earn,
   all-surpassing gift
   of righteousness.

3. Oh, to know the pow'r
   of your risen life,
   and to know you in
   your sufferings.
   To become like you
   in your death, my Lord,
   so with you to live
   and never die.

9 All my days

(Beautiful Saviour)

Words and Music: Stuart Townend

1. All my days I will sing this song of glad - ness,
2. I will trust in the cross of my Re - dee - mer,

give my praise to the Foun - tain of De - lights;
I will sing of the blood that ne - ver fails,

help - less - ness you heard my cry, and waves of
giv - en, of con - science cleansed, of death de -

mer - cy poured down on my life.
fea - ted and life with - out end.

Beau - ti - ful

3. I long to be where the praise is never-ending,
   yearn to dwell where the glory never fades,
   where countless worshippers will share one song,
   and cries of 'worthy' will honour the Lamb!

10 All praise, all honour

(All praise)

Words and Music: James Wright

All praise, all hon-our, all strength, wis-dom and pow - er: Je - sus, be en- throned up-on our wor - ship and our praise. All Je - sus, the Name a-bove all

11 All shall be well!

Words: Timothy Dudley-Smith

Music: Orlando Gibbons

1. All shall be well! for on our Eas - ter skies

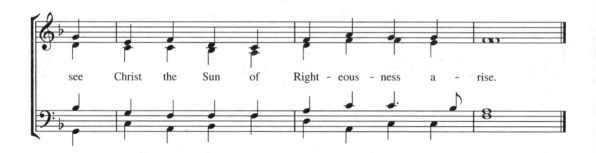

see Christ the Sun of Right - eous - ness a - rise.

2. All shall be well! the sacrifice is made;
   the sinner freed, the price of pardon paid.

3. All shall be well! the cross and passion past;
   dark night is done, bright morning come at last.

4. All shall be well! within our Father's plan
   death has no more dominion over man.

5. Jesus alive! Rejoice and sing again,
   'All shall be well for evermore, Amen!'

12 All ye that pass by

Words: Charles Wesley

Music: William Knapp
arr. Chris Mitchell

WAREHAM LM

2. He dies to atone
   for sins not his own;
   your debt he hath paid,
   and your work he hath done.
   Ye all may receive
   the peace he did leave,
   who made intercession:
   my Father, forgive!

3. For you and for me
   he prayed on the tree:
   the pray'r is accepted,
   the sinner is free.
   That sinner am I,
   who on Jesus rely,
   and come for the pardon
   God cannot deny.

4. My pardon I claim;
   for a sinner I am,
   a sinner believing
   in Jesus's name.
   He purchased the grace
   which now I embrace:
   O Father, thou know'st
   he hath died in my place.

13 All you who seek a comfort sure

Words: *Quincunque centum quæritis*
trans Edward Caswall, alt. the editors

Music: Adapted from a melody
in *Tochter Sion*

ST BERNARD CM

1. All you who seek a com-fort sure in trou-ble and dis-tress, what-e-ver sor-row vex the mind, or guilt the soul op-press.

2. Jesus, who gave himself for you
   upon the cross to die,
   opens to you his sacred heart;
   O, to that heart draw nigh.

3. You hear how kindly he invites;
   you hear his words so blest:
   'All you that labour, come to me,
   and I will give you rest.'

4. What meeker than the Saviour's heart?
   As on the cross he lay,
   it did his murderers forgive,
   and for their pardon pray.

5. Jesus, the joy of saints on high,
   the hope of sinners here,
   attracted by those loving words
   to you I lift my prayer.

6. Wash then my wounds in that dear blood
   which forth from you does flow;
   by grace a better hope inspire,
   and risen life bestow.

14 A man there lived in Galilee

Words: Somerset Corry Lowry

Music: Tyrolean melody
arr. Richard Lloyd

TYROL DCM

1. A man there lived in Ga-li-lee like none who lived be-fore, for
he a-lone from first to last our flesh un-sul-lied wore; a
per-fect life of per-fect deeds once to the world was shown, that
peo-ple all might mark his steps and in them plant their own.

2. A man there died on Calvary
   above all others brave;
   the human race he saved and blessed,
   himself he scorned to save.
   No thought can gauge the weight of woe
   on him, the sinless, laid;
   we only know that with his blood
   our ransom price was paid.

3. A man there reigns in glory now,
   divine, yet human still;
   that human which is all divine
   death sought in vain to kill.
   All pow'r is his; supreme he rules
   the realms of time and space;
   yet still our human cares and needs
   find in his heart a place.

15 And can it be

Words: Charles Wesley | Music: Thomas Campbell

SAGINA 88 88 88 extended

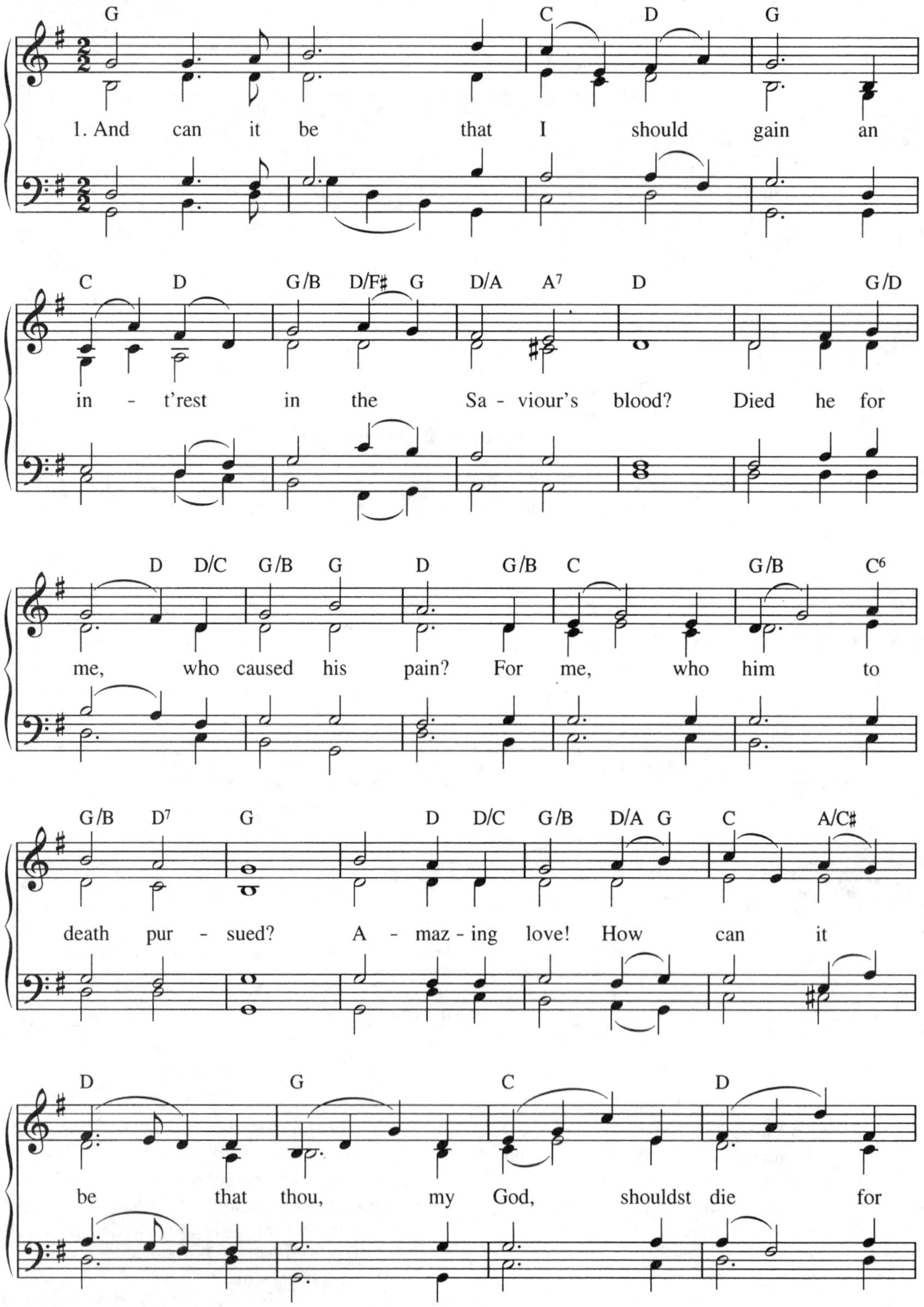
G C D G
1. And can it be that I should gain an
C D G/B D/F# G D/A A7 D G/D
in - t'rest in the Sa - viour's blood? Died he for
D D/C G/B G D G/B C G/B C6
me, who caused his pain? For me, who him to
G/B D7 G D D/C G/B D/A G C A/C#
death pur - sued? A - maz - ing love! How can it
D G C D
be that thou, my God, shouldst die for

2. 'Tis myst'ry all! th'Immortal dies:
who can explore his strange design?
In vain the first-born seraph tries
to sound the depths of love divine!
'Tis mercy all! Let earth adore,
let angel minds inquire no more.

3. He left his Father's throne above
so free, so infinite his grace;
emptied himself of all but love,
and bled for Adam's helpless race;
'tis mercy all, immense and free;
for, O my God, it found out me.

4. Long my imprisoned spirit lay
fast bound in sin and nature's night;
thine eye diffused a quick'ning ray,
I woke, the dungeon flamed with light;
my chains fell off, my heart was free;
I rose, went forth, and followed thee.

5. No condemnation now I dread;
Jesus, and all in him is mine!
Alive in him, my living Head,
and clothed in righteousness divine,
bold I approach the eternal throne,
and claim the crown, through Christ my own.

16 And he shall reign

Words and Music: Graham Kendrick

And he shall reign for e - ver, his throne and crown shall e - ver en - dure. And he shall reign for e - ver, and we shall reign with him.

2. He was given sov'reign power,
   glory and authority.
   Every nation, tribe and tongue
   worshipped him on bended knee.

3. On the throne for ever,
   see the Lamb who once was slain;
   wounds of sacrificial love
   for ever shall remain.

17 A purple robe

Words: Timothy Dudley-Smith

Music: David Wilson arr. Noel Tredinnick

1. A pur - ple robe, a crown of thorn, a reed in his right
4. He hangs, by whom the world was made, be - neath the dark - ened

hand; be - fore the sol - diers' spite and scorn I
sky; the e - ver - last - ing ran - som paid, I

see my Sa - viour stand. 2. He bears be - tween the
see my Sa - viour die. 5. He shares on high his

Ro - man guard the weight of all our woe; a
Fa - ther's throne who once in mer - cy came; for

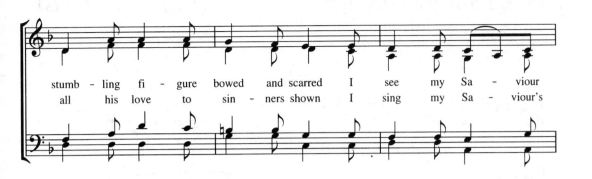

stumb - ling fi - gure bowed and scarred I see my Sa - viour
all his love to sin - ners shown I sing my Sa - viour's

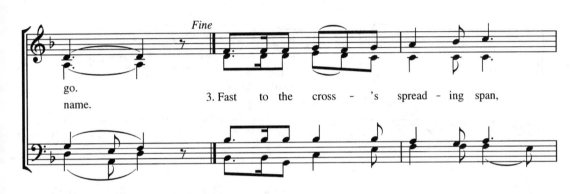

Fine

go.
name. 3. Fast to the cross - 's spread - ing span,

high in the sun - lit air, all the un - num - bered

D.C. al Fine

sins of man I see my Sa - viour bear.

18 A rainfall in drought *(By your wounds)*

Words and Music: Anju Ebanks

1. A rain - fall in drought, the birth of the King.

the shed blood of God.
who knew your pain?

You had no beau - ty to draw us
Your bo - dy pierced, your spi - rit
The an - guish suf - fered for all man -

near.
crushed.
kind.

2. The price for our peace,

O Lord, you've re-vealed your re - deem - ing

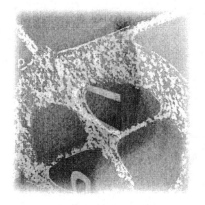

19 A stranger walked along the shore

(Worship the King)

Words and Music: Roger Jones
arr. Chris Mitchell

1. A stran-ger walked a-long the shore of Ga-li-lee.
He met two fish-er-men, and then cried 'Fol-low me!'
They left their nets, and then he taught them to catch men. They watched him as he died and rose a-gain!
It was the King! Wor-ship the King!

2. The stranger walked along the road to Calvary.
   They nailed him to a cross of wood
   so cruelly.
   The women watched and cried,
   the blood flowed from his side,
   the sun stopped shining as the Saviour died!
   It was the King!

3. When Mary came to see the tomb, so early,
   the stone was moved, his body gone!
   'Where can it be?'
   A voice came from behind,
   it sounded, oh, so kind,
   then suddenly it dawned upon her mind –
   it was the King!

20 As we come to your throne   *(You are worthy)*

Words and Music: Andrew Grinnell
arr. Richard Lewis

21 At the foot of the cross

Words and Music: Derek Bond

With a gentle rhythm

At the foot of the cross, I can hard-ly take it in, that the King of all cre-a-tion was dy-ing for my sin. And the pain and a-go-ny, and the thorns that pierced your head, and the hard-ness of my sin-ful heart that left you there for dead.

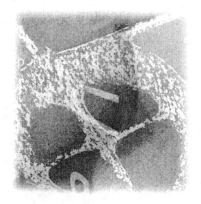

22 At the Lamb's high feast we sing

Words: *Ad regias Agni dapes*
trans. Robert Campbell
SALZBURG 77 77 D

Music: Jacob Hintze harmony by
Johann Sebastian Bach

1. At the Lamb's high feast we sing praise to our vic-tor-ious King, who hath washed us in the tide flow-ing from his pier-cèd side; praise we him, whose love di-vine gives his sa-cred blood for wine, gives his bo-dy for the feast, Christ the vic-tim, Christ the priest.

2. Where the paschal blood is poured,
death's dark angel sheathes his sword;
faithful hosts triumphant go
through the wave that drowns the foe.
Praise we Christ, whose blood was shed,
paschal victim, paschal bread;
with sincerity and love
eat we manna from above.

3. Mighty victim from above,
conqu'ring by the pow'r of love;
thou hast triumphed in the fight,
thou hast brought us life and light.
Now no more can death appal,
now no more the grave enthral:
thou hast opened paradise,
and in thee thy saints shall rise.

4. Easter triumph, Easter joy,
nothing now can this destroy;
from sin's pow'r do thou set free
souls new-born, O Lord, in thee.
Hymns of glory and of praise,
risen Lord, to thee we raise;
holy Father, praise to thee,
with the Spirit, ever be.

23 At the name of Jesus

Words: Caroline Maria Noel, alt.

Music: Michael Brierley

2. At his voice creation
   sprang at once to sight,
   all the angel faces,
   all the hosts of light,
   thrones and dominations,
   stars upon their way,
   all the heav'nly orders
   in their great array.

3. Humbled for a season,
   to receive a name
   from the lips of sinners
   unto whom he came,
   faithfully he bore it,
   spotless to the last,
   brought it back victorious
   when from death he passed.

4. Bore it up triumphant,
   with its human light,
   through all ranks of creatures
   to the central height,
   to the throne of Godhead,
   to the Father's breast,
   filled it with the glory
   of that perfect rest.

5. All creation, name him,
   with love as strong as death;
   but with awe and wonder,
   and with bated breath.
   He is God the Saviour,
   he is Christ the Lord,
   ever to be worshipped,
   trusted and adored.

6. In your hearts enthrone him;
   there let him subdue
   all that is not holy,
   all that is not true;
   crown him as your captain
   in temptation's hour;
   let his will enfold you
   in its light and pow'r.

7. Truly, this Lord Jesus
   shall return again,
   with his Father's glory,
   with his angel train;
   for all wreaths of empire
   meet upon his brow,
   and our hearts confess him
   King of glory now.

24 At your feet we fall

Words and Music: David Fellingham

With steady strength

1. At your feet we fall, migh-ty ri-sen Lord, as we come be-fore your throne to wor-ship you. By your Spi-rit's pow'r you now draw our hearts, and we hear your voice in

2. There we see you stand, mighty risen Lord,
   clothed in garments pure and holy, shining bright.
   Eyes of flashing fire, feet like burnished bronze,
   and the sound of many waters is your voice.

3. Like the shining sun in its noonday strength,
   we now see the glory of your wondrous face.
   Once that face was marred, but now you're glorified,
   and your words like a two-edged sword have mighty pow'r.

25 Behold his love

Words and Music: Geoff Baker

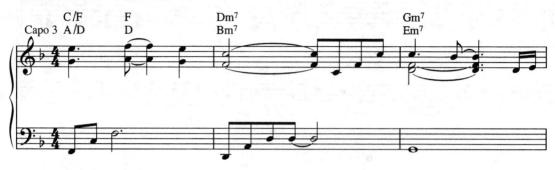

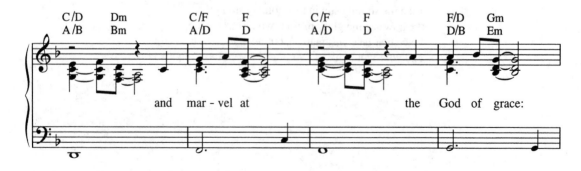

26 Behold, I am the first and the last

Words and Music: Steve James

Gently, building in the chorus

Be - hold, I am the first and the last, I am the liv- ing one, I died, now I'm a - live e - ver - more!

27 Behold the Lamb

Words and Music: Mark Altrogge

1. Be-hold the Lamb, sil-ent be-fore his ac-cu-sers as thorns are pressed in-to his brow.
2. Be-hold the Lamb, car-ry-ing all our trans-gres-sions, he free-ly takes our place;

They lift him up, oh see the spikes that hold him, re-deem-ing blood flows down.
en-dures the lash, the mock-ing and the laugh-ter of those he dies to save.

28 Behold the Saviour of mankind

Words: Samuel Wesley

Music: Chetham's *Psalmody*

BURFORD CM

1. Be - hold the Sa - viour of man - kind nailed to the shame - ful tree! How vast the love that him in - clined to bleed and die for thee!

2. Hark, how he groans! while nature shakes,
   and earth's strong pillars bend;
   the temple's veil in sunder breaks,
   the solid marbles rend.

3. 'Tis done! the precious ransom's paid;
   receive my soul! he cries:
   see where he bows his sacred head!
   He bows his head, and dies!

4. But soon he'll break death's envious chain,
   and in full glory shine:
   O Lamb of God, was ever pain,
   was ever love like thine?

29 Beneath the cross of Jesus

Words: Elizabeth C. Clephane alt.

Music: Frederick C. Maker

SAINT CHRISTOPHER 76 86 86 86

1. Be-neath the cross of Je-sus I fain would take my stand, the sha-dow of a might-y rock with-in a wea-ry land; a home with-in a wil-der-ness, a rest up-on the way, from burn-ing heat at noon-tide and the bur-den of the day.

2. O safe and happy shelter!
   O refuge tried and sweet!
   O trysting place where heaven's love
   and heaven's justice meet!
   As to the holy patriarch
   that wondrous dream was giv'n,
   so seems my Saviour's cross to me
   a ladder up to heav'n.

3. There lies, beneath its shadow
   but on the farther side,
   the darkness of an awful grave
   that gapes both deep and wide;
   and there between us stands the cross,
   two arms outstretched to save;
   a watchman set to guard the way
   from that eternal grave.

4. Upon that cross of Jesus
   mine eye at times can see
   the very dying form of One
   who suffered there for me;
   and from my stricken heart, with tears,
   two wonders I confess –
   the wonders of redeeming love,
   and my unworthiness.

5. I take, O cross, thy shadow
   for my abiding place!
   I ask no other sunshine than
   the sunshine of his face;
   content to let the world go by,
   to reckon gain as loss –
   my sinful self, my only shame,
   my glory all – the cross.

30 Broken for me

Words and Music: Janet Lunt

2. Come to my table and with me dine;
   eat of my bread and drink of my wine.

3. This is my body given for you;
   eat it remembering I died for you.

4. This is my blood I shed for you,
   for your forgiveness, making you new.

31 Christ is risen

Words and Music: Chris Rolinson

Joyfully ♩. = 76

Chorus

Christ is ri - sen — hal - le - lu - jah, hal - le - lu - jah!

Christ is ri - sen, ri - sen in - deed — hal - le - lu — jah!

1. Love's work is done, the bat - tle is won. Where now, O death, is your
2. Lord o - ver sin, Lord o - ver death, at his feet Sa - tan must
3. Tell it a - broad, 'Je - sus is Lord!' Shout it and let your praise

sting?   He rose a - gain to rule and to reign,
fall!   Ev - ery knee, bow! All will con - fess
ring!   Glad - ly we raise our songs of praise –

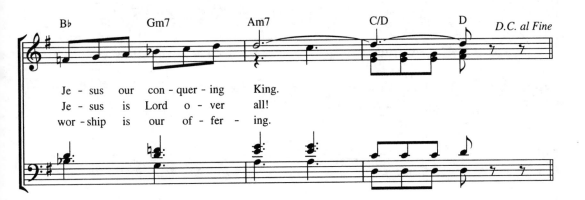

Je - sus our con - quer - ing King.
Je - sus is Lord o - ver all!
wor - ship is our of - fer - ing.

D.C. al Fine

32 Christ is risen! Raise your voices

Words: Frank von Christierson

Music: Cyril Taylor

MEADHOUSE 87 87 D

1. Christ is ri-sen! Raise your voi-ces ju-bi-lant with joy and praise.
Christ is ri-sen! Earth re-joi-ces! To the Lord your an-thems raise.
O-ver sin and death vic-to-rious, Christ is ri-sen! Hail your King!
E-ver may his praise be glo-rious; let the world his tri-umph sing!

2. Lord of life, our Saviour risen,
bid the shadows flee away;
death no more a darkened prison,
death the door to life's new day.
This the resurrection chorus,
lift its music on the air:
Jesus lives, our Lord victorious,
Tell it! Tell it ev'rywhere.

3. Life eternal! Joy of heaven;
life abundant – joy of earth;
life which God in Christ has given
brings to us new hope, new worth.
Lift your hearts from sin and sadness,
trust this joyful sacred word,
fill the earth with holy gladness:
Christ is risen! Christ our Lord!

33 Christ the Lord is risen again

Words: after Michael Weisse, Catherine Winkworth

Music: *Hundert Arien* Dresden

1. Christ the Lord is risen a-gain,
   Christ has bro-ken ev-ery chain;
   hear the an-gel voi-ces cry,
   sing-ing e-ver-more on high:
   Al - le - lu - ia!

2. He who gave for us his life,
   who for us en-dured the strife,
   is our pas-chal lamb to-day;
   we too sing for joy and say:
   Al - le - lu - ia!

3. He who bore all pain and loss
   com-fort-less up-on the cross
   lives in glo-ry now on high,
   pleads for us and hears our cry:
   Al - le - lu - ia!

4. He who slumbered in the grave
   is exalted now to save;
   through the universe it rings
   that the lamb is King of kings:
   Alleluia!

5. Now he bids us tell abroad
   how the lost may be restored,
   how the penitent forgiven,
   how we too may enter heaven:
   Alleluia!

6. Christ, our paschal lamb indeed,
   all your ransomed people feed!
   take our sins and guilt away;
   let us sing by night and day:
   Alleluia!

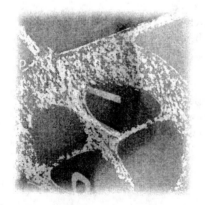

34 Christ triumphant

Words: Michael Saward

Music: Michael Baughen

CHRIST TRIUMPHANT 85 85 and Refrain

1. Christ triumphant, ever reigning, Saviour, Master, King.
Lord of heav'n, our lives sustaining, hear us as we sing:

Chorus
Yours the glory and the crown, the high renown, the eternal name.

2. Word incarnate, truth revealing,
Son of Man on earth!
Pow'r and majesty concealing
by your humble birth:

3. Suff'ring servant, scorned, ill-treated,
victim crucified!
Death is through the cross defeated,
sinners justified:

4. Priestly King, enthroned for ever
high in heav'n above!
Sin and death and hell shall never
stifle hymns of love:

5. So, our hearts and voices raising
through the ages long,
ceaselessly upon you gazing,
this shall be our song:

35 Come and join in the song

(He's alive!)

Words and Music: Mark and Helen Johnson
arr. Donald Thomson

2. Ev'ry knee shall bow to him,
   and ev'ryone confess:
   Jesus Christ is Lord and King,
   he's conquered sin and death!

3. Ev'ry nation, ev'ry tribe
   will glorify his name.
   All creation shall bow down
   and honour him with praise!

36 Come and see

(We worship at your feet)

Words and Music: Graham Kendrick

Worshipfully

1. Come and see, come and see, come and see the King of love; see the pur-ple robe and crown of thorns he wears. Sol-diers mock, ru-lers sneer as he lifts the cru-el cross; lone and friend-less now, he climbs to-wards the hill. *Chorus* We wor-ship at your feet, where wrath and mer-cy meet, and a

2. Come and weep, come and mourn
   for your sin that pierced him there;
   so much deeper than the wounds of thorn and nail.
   All our pride, all our greed,
   all our fallenness and shame;
   and the Lord has laid the punishment on him.

3. Man of heaven, born to earth
   to restore us to your heaven.
   Here we bow in awe beneath your searching eyes.
   From your tears comes our joy,
   from your death our life shall spring;
   by your resurrection power we shall rise.

37 Come and sing

Words and Music: Mike Burn
arr. Donald Thomson

1. Come and sing, come and sing, come and sing to Je - sus now. Come and sing, come and sing, come and sing to Je - sus now. Give him thanks for who he is, give him thanks for what he's done, come and sing.

Chorus Je -

- sus won it all for us when he shed his blood on the cross.

Sin and death were swal-lowed up, they don't have a hold on us now, that's the rea - son to sing.

2. Come and dance,

2. Come and dance, come and dance,
   come and dance for Jesus now.
   Come and dance, come and dance,
   come and dance for Jesus now.
   Dance for joy before the throne,
   let your inhibitions go,
   come and dance.

38 Come, let us with our Lord arise

Words: Charles Wesley

Music: William Matthews

MADRID 88 88 88

1. Come, let us with our Lord a - rise,

our Lord, who made both earth and skies:

who died to save the world he made,

and rose, tri - umph - ant from the dead; he

rose, the Prince of life and peace, and

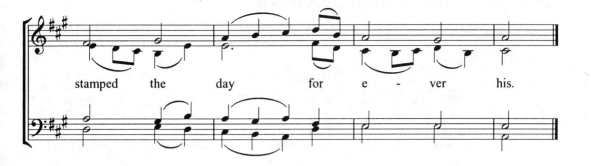

stamped the day for e - ver his.

2. This is the day the Lord has made,
   that all may see his love displayed,
   may feel his resurrection's pow'r,
   and rise again, to fall no more,
   in perfect righteousness renewed,
   and filled with all the life of God.

3. Then let us render him his own,
   with solemn prayer approach his throne,
   with meekness hear the gospel word,
   with thanks his dying love record,
   our joyful hearts and voices raise,
   and fill his courts with songs of praise.

4. Honour and praise to Jesus pay
   throughout his consecrated day;
   be all in Jesus' praise employed,
   nor leave a single moment void;
   with utmost care the time improve,
   and only breathe his praise and love.

39 Crown him with many crowns

Words: Matthew Bridges

Music: George Job Elvey

DIADEMATA DSM

1. Crown him with ma-ny crowns, the Lamb up-on his throne; hark, how the heav'n-ly an-them drowns all mu-sic but its own: a - wake, my soul, and sing of him who died for thee, and hail him as thy match-less King through all e-ter-ni - ty.

2. Crown him the Lord of life,
   who triumphed o'er the grave,
   and rose victorious in the strife
   for those he came to save.
   His glories now we sing,
   who died and rose on high,
   who died eternal life to bring,
   and lives that death may die.

3. Crown him the Lord of love;
   behold his hands and side,
   rich wounds, yet visible above,
   in beauty glorified:
   no angel in the sky
   can fully bear that sight,
   but downward bends each burning eye
   at mysteries so bright.

4. Crown him the Lord of peace,
   whose pow'r a sceptre sways
   from pole to pole, that wars may cease,
   and all be prayer and praise:
   his reign shall know no end,
   and round his piercèd feet
   fair flow'rs of paradise extend
   their fragrance ever sweet.

5. Crown him the Lord of years,
   the Potentate of time,
   Creator of the rolling spheres,
   ineffably sublime.
   All hail, Redeemer, hail!
   for thou hast died for me;
   thy praise shall never, never fail
   throughout eternity.

40 Day of wrath and day of wonder

Words: Michael Forster

Music: Traditional Welsh melody
arr. Colin Hand

AR HYD Y NOS 84 84 88 84

1. Day of wrath and day of won - der, whence hope has fled!

See the bo - dy torn a -sun - der, blood free - ly shed.

Stripped of ma - jes - ty we saw him, hu -man sight re - coiled be -fore him,

yet it was our sor - rows tore him; for us he bled.

2. Day of hope and day of glory,
   though unperceived!
   See redemption's dreadful story,
   long, long conceived.
   Evil pow'rs, in downfall lying,
   knowing death itself is dying,
   hear the voice triumphant crying,
   'All is achieved!'

3. Day of majesty and splendour,
   here ends the race!
   Christ, our Priest, our soul's defender,
   us will embrace.
   He who walked this earth before us,
   tried and tempted, yet victorious,
   calls us to the kingdom glorious,
   O perfect grace!

41 Don't let me waste your sacrifice

Words and Music: Susie Hare

1. Don't let me waste your sac - ri - fice, don't let me waste your
2. When I for - get to see your throne, show me the thorns that

sin - less life; all that I am must al - ways be
made your crown; when I for - get the tears you cried,

wor - thy of all you gave for me. When I for - get the
show me the wounds that marred your side. You did - n't die that

Fa - ther's loss, lift up my eyes to see your cross;
I might still hold to a life that binds your will;

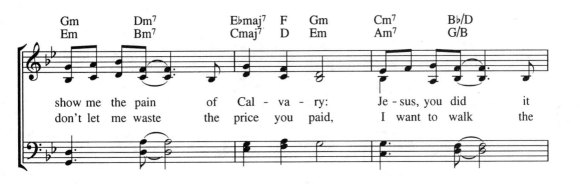

show me the pain of Cal - va - ry: Je - sus, you did it
don't let me waste the price you paid, I want to walk the

Chorus

all for me.
path you made. I want to re-build the al - tar of

my heart, give you my first and give you my last,

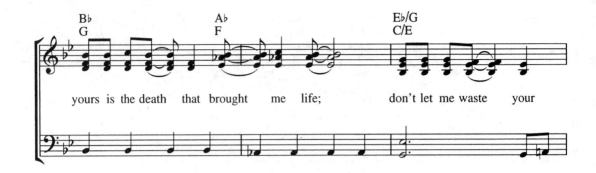

yours is the death that brought me life; don't let me waste your

sac - ri - fice, don't let me waste your sac - ri - fice.

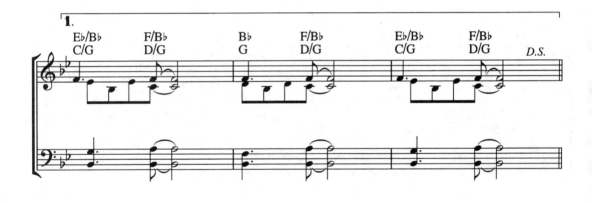

1.

D.S.

2.

I want to re - build the al - tar of my heart,

42 Easter jubilation

Words and Music: Mark and Helen Johnson

With pace

1. Eas-ter ju-bi-la-tion fills the streets and towns,
ce - le -bra-tions have be - gun. Hear the mu-sic and the
dan - cing now, join the laugh-ter and the fun!

Chorus

Oh, raise a joy - ful shout!

Clap your hands and dance, let your feel - ings out.

Oh, hear what it's a-bout: Christ, the Lord, has come to

To repeat

set us free.

Last time

set us free! Hoy!

2. Put aside your sorrows, wipe your tears away,
   for a better time will come.
   There's a promise of a better day,
   join the laughter and the fun!

3. La, la, la, la, la, etc,

4. Easter jubilation fills the streets and towns,
   celebrations have begun.
   Hear the music and the dancing now,
   join the laughter and the fun!

43 Filled with compassion

(For all the people who live on the earth)

Words and Music: Noel and Tricia Richards

Gently

1. Filled with com-pas-sion for all cre-a-tion,
Je-sus came in-to a world that was lost.
There was but one way that he could save us,
on-ly through suf-fer-ing death on a cross.

Chorus

God, you are wait-ing, your heart is break-ing

for all the peo - ple who live on the earth.

Stir us to ac - tion, filled with your pas - sion

for all the peo - ple who live on the earth.

Last time

2. Great is your passion for all the people
   living and dying without knowing you.
   Having no saviour, they're lost for ever,
   if we don't speak out and lead them to you.

3. From ev'ry nation we shall be gathered,
   millions redeemed shall be Jesus' reward.
   Then he will turn and say to his Father:
   'Truly my suffering was worth it all.'

44 For this purpose

Words and Music: Graham Kendrick

Lyrics beneath the music:

1. For this pur - pose Christ was re - veal'd to des - troy all the works of the ev - il one. Christ in us has o - ver - come, so with glad-ness we sing and wel-come his king-dom in.

2. In the name of Jesus we stand,
   by the power of his blood
   we now claim this ground.
   Satan has no authority here,
   pow'rs of darkness must flee,
   for Christ has the victory.

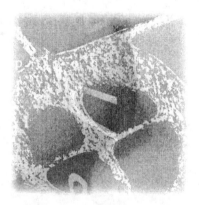

45 Forty days and forty nights

Words: George Hunt Smyttan
adapted by Michael Forster

Music: Melody from
Nürnbergisches Gesangbuch

AUS DER TIEFE (HEINLEIN) 77 77

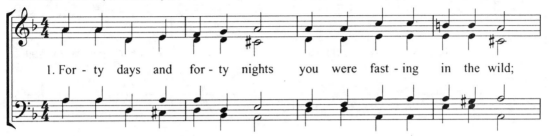

1. For - ty days and for - ty nights you were fast - ing in the wild;

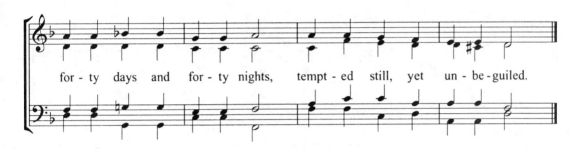

for - ty days and for - ty nights, tempt - ed still, yet un - be - guiled.

2. Sunbeams scorching all the day,
   chilly dew-drops nightly shed,
   prowling beasts about your way,
   stones your pillow, earth your bed.

3. Let us your endurance share,
   and from earthly greed abstain,
   with you vigilant in prayer,
   with you strong to suffer pain.

4. Then if evil on us press,
   flesh or spirit to assail,
   Victor in the wilderness,
   help us not to swerve or fail.

5. So shall peace divine be ours;
   holy gladness, pure and true:
   come to us, angelic powers,
   such as ministered to you.

6. Keep, O keep us, Saviour dear,
   ever constant by your side,
   that with you we may appear
   at th'eternal Eastertide.

46 From heaven you came

(The Servant King)

Words and Music: Graham Kendrick

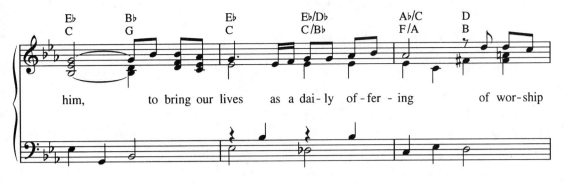

him, to bring our lives as a dai-ly of-fer-ing of wor-ship

To next verse

Last time

to the Ser-vant King.

King.

2. There in the garden of tears,
   my heavy load he chose to bear;
   his heart with sorrow was torn.
   'Yet not my will but yours,' he said.

3. Come see his hands and his feet,
   the scars that speak of sacrifice,
   hands that flung stars into space,
   to cruel nails surrendered.

4. So let us learn how to serve,
   and in our lives enthrone him;
   each other's needs to prefer,
   for it is Christ we're serving.

47 From the heights of glory

(What a gift)

Words and Music: Susie Hare

2. From a humble stable, to a world of shame,
   the friend of sinners, who calls my name
   brought the love of heaven to the hearts of men
   and it gave lives hope again.

3. From a life, so perfect, to a cruel cross,
   the world's redemption, the Father's loss;
   and the nails were driven and the blood flowed free
   in the hands outstretched for me.

4. From the grave he's risen, ever glorified,
   to take his place at his Father's side;
   and the greatest glory will be ours to own
   when he comes to take us home.

What a hope, what a hope we are given,
sacrifice of the Father for us.
What a song to proclaim: 'He is risen!
King of kings, Lord of lords, Jesus!
King of kings, Lord of lords, Jesus!

48 From the squalor of a borrowed stable

Words and Music: Stuart Townend

(Immanuel)

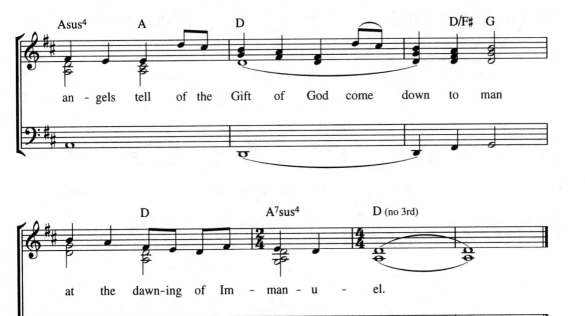

an - gels tell of the Gift of God come down to man

at the dawn-ing of Im - man - u - el.

2. King of heaven now the friend of sinners,
   humble servant in the Father's hands,
   filled with power and the Holy Spirit,
   filled with mercy for the broken man.
   Yes, he walked my road and he felt my pain,
   joys and sorrows that I know so well;
   yet his righteous steps give me hope again –
   I will follow my Immanuel!

3. Through the kisses of a friend's betrayal,
   he was lifted on a cruel cross;
   he was punished for a world's transgressions,
   he was suffering to save the lost.
   He fights for breath, he fights for me,
   loosing sinners from the claims of hell;
   and with a shout our souls are free –
   death defeated by Immanuel!

4. Now he's standing in the place of honour,
   crowned with glory on the highest throne,
   interceding for his own belovèd
   till his Father calls to bring them home!
   Then the skies will part as the trumpet sounds
   hope of heaven or the fear of hell;
   but the Bride will run to her Lover's arms,
   giving glory to Immanuel!

49 God sent his Son

(Because he lives)

Words and Music: Gloria Gaither and William J. Gaither

1. God sent his Son, they called him Je-sus; he came to love, heal and for-give. He lived and died to buy my par-don; an emp-ty grave is there to prove my Sa-viour lives.

Chorus

Be-cause he lives I can face to-

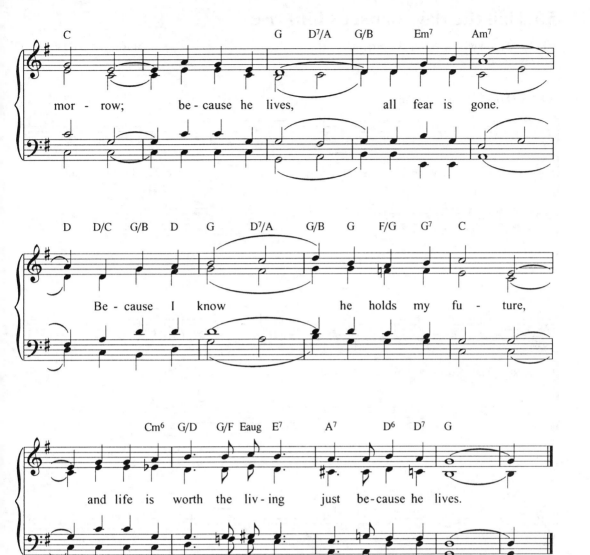

mor - row; be - cause he lives, all fear is gone.

Be - cause I know he holds my fu - ture,

and life is worth the liv - ing just be - cause he lives.

2. How sweet to hold a new-born baby,
   and feel the pride and joy he gives;
   but greater still the calm assurance:
   this child can face uncertain days because he lives.

3. And then one day I'll cross the river;
   I'll fight life's final war with pain.
   And then, as death gives way to vict'ry,
   I'll see the lights of glory and I'll know he reigns.

50 Hail the day that sees him rise

Words: Charles Wesley, Thomas Cotterill
and others, alt.

Music: Robert Williams

LLANFAIR 77 77 and Alleluias

1. Hail the day that sees him rise, al - le - lu - ia!
to his throne a - bove the skies; al - le - lu - ia!
Christ the Lamb, for sin - ners giv'n, al - le - lu - ia!
en - ters now the high - est heav'n! al - le - lu - ia!

2. There for him high triumph waits;
   lift your heads, eternal gates!
   He hath conquered death and sin;
   take the King of Glory in!

3. Circled round with angel-pow'rs,
   their triumphant Lord and ours;
   wide unfold the radiant scene,
   take the King of Glory in!

4. Lo, the heav'n its Lord receives,
   yet he loves the earth he leaves;
   though returning to his throne,
   calls the human race his own.

5. See, he lifts his hands above;
   see, he shows the prints of love;
   hark, his gracious lips bestow
   blessings on his Church below.

6. Still for us he intercedes,
   his prevailing death he pleads;
   near himself prepares our place,
   he the first-fruits of our race.

7. Lord, though parted from our sight,
   far above the starry height,
   grant our hearts may thither rise,
   seeking thee above the skies.

8. Ever upward let us move,
   wafted on the wings of love;
   looking when our Lord shall come,
   longing, sighing after home.

51 Hallelujah, hallelujah   *(The Lord Almighty reigns)*

Words and Music: Terry Butler

52 Hallelujah! Jesus is alive

Words and Music: Ron Kenoly

Hal-le-lu-jah! Je-sus is a-live, death has lost its vic-t'ry and the grave has been de-nied; Je-sus lives for-e-ver, he's a-live! he's a-live! He's the Al-pha and O-me-ga, the first and last is he,

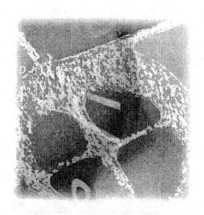

53 Hallelujah, my Father

Words and Music: Tim Cullen

Hal-le-lu-jah, my Fa-ther, for giv-ing us your Son;

send-ing him in-to the world to be gi-ven up for all.

Know-ing we would bruise him and smite him from the earth. Hal-le-

lu-jah, my Fa-ther, in his death is my birth; hal-le-

lu-jah, my Fa-ther, in his life is my life.

54 Hark! the voice of love and mercy

Words: Jonathan Evans and in this
version Jubilate Hymns

Music: Henry Smart, last verse
arrangements and descant John Barnard

REGENT SQUARE

1. Hark! the voice of love and mer-cy sounds a-loud from Cal-va-ry;
2. Fi-nished – all the types and sha-dows of the ce-re-mo-nial law;

see, it tears the tem-ple cur-tain, shakes the earth and veils the sky:
God ful-fils what he has pro-mised – death and hell shall reign no more:

'It is fi-nished, it is fi-nished!' – hear the dy-ing Sa-viour cry.
'It is fi-nished, it is fi-nished!' – Christ has o-pened hea-ven's door.

Descant

3. Saints and an-gels shout his prai-ses, his great fi-nished work pro-claim;

Unison

Words: © in this version Jubilate Hymns
Music: last verse arrangement and descant © John Barnard / Jubilate Hymns,
4 Thorne Park Road, Chelston, Torquay TQ2 6RX, UK. Used by permission.

all on earth and all in hea - ven join to bless Em - ma - nuel's name:

'Al - le - lu - ia, al - le - lu - ia, end - less glo - ry to the Lamb!'

55 He has risen

Words and Music: Gerald Coates, Noel Richards and Tricia Richards

He has ri - sen, he has ri - sen, he has ri - sen, Je - sus is a-live.

1. When the life flowed from his bo - dy, seemed like Je - sus' mis - sion failed.

But his sac - ri - fice ac -
com - plished, vic - t'ry o -
- ver sin and hell.

D.C. al Fine

2. In the grave God did not leave him,
   for his body to decay;
   raised to life, the great awakening,
   Satan's pow'r he overcame.

3. If there were no resurrection,
   we ourselves could not be raised;
   but the Son of God is living,
   so our hope is not in vain.

4. When the Lord rides out of heaven,
   mighty angels at his side,
   they will sound the final trumpet,
   from the grave we shall arise.

5. He has given life immortal,
   we shall see him face to face;
   through eternity we'll praise him,
   Christ the champion of our faith.

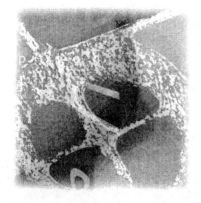

56 He is Lord

Words and Music: Unknown

57 Here I am   *(I will always love your name)*

Words and Music: Paul Oakley

Rhythmically

1. Here I am, and I have come to thank you, Lord, for all you've done: thank you, Lord; you paid the price at Cal-va-ry, you shed your blood, you set me free: thank you, Lord; no

great-er love was e-ver shown, no bet-ter life e-ver
was laid down.
And I
will al-ways love your name;
and I will al-ways sing your praise;
and I
2. You
3. You

2. You took my sin, you took my shame,
   you drank my cup, you bore my pain:
   thank you, Lord;
   you broke the curse, you broke the chains,
   in victory from death you rose again:
   thank you, Lord;
   and not by works, but by your grace
   you clothe me now in your righteousness.

3. You bid me come, you make me whole,
   you give me peace, you restore my soul:
   thank you, Lord;
   you fill me up, and when I'm full
   you give me more till I overflow:
   thank you, Lord;
   you're making me to be like you,
   to do the works of the Father, too.

58 Here is bread

Words and Music: Graham Kendrick

1. Here is bread, here is wine, Christ is with us, he is with us. Break the bread, taste the wine, Christ is with us here.

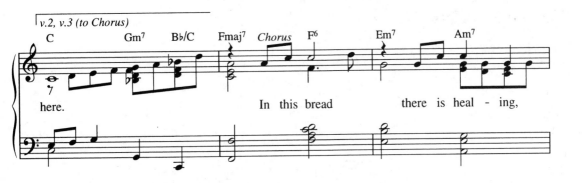

2. Here is grace, here is peace,
   Christ is with us, he is with us;
   know his grace, find his peace,
   feast on Jesus here.

3. Here we are, joined in one,
   Christ is with us, he is with us;
   we'll proclaim till he comes
   Jesus crucified.

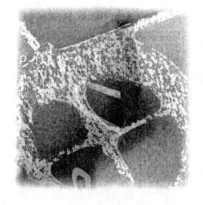

59 Here is love

Words: William Rees

Music: Robert Lowry

DIM OND IESU

1. Here is love vast as the o-cean, lov-ing kind-ness as the flood. When the
Prince of Life, our ran-som, shed for us his pre-cious blood. Who his
love will not re-mem-ber? Who can cease to sing his praise? He can
ne-ver be for-got-ten, through-out heav'n's e-ter-nal days.

2. On the mount of crucifixion
fountains opened deep and wide;
through the floodgates of God's mercy
flowed a vast and gracious tide.
Grace and love, like mighty rivers,
poured incessant from above,
and heaven's peace and perfect justice
kissed a guilty world in love.

60 Here is the risen Son

Words and Music: Michael Sandeman

61 He that is in us

Words and Music: Graham Kendrick

I will re-joice for his Spi - rit lives in me.

Christ the liv - ing one has o - ver -

come and we share in his vic - to - ry.

2. All the powers of death and hell and sin
   lie crushed beneath his feet.
   Jesus owns the name above all names,
   crowned with honour and majesty.

62 He was pierced

(Like a lamb)

Words and Music: Maggi Dawn

Thoughtful

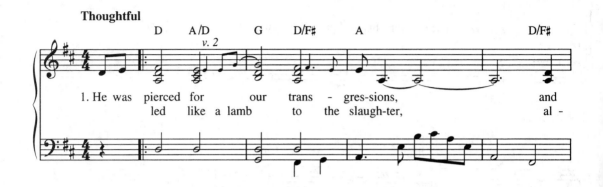

1. He was pierced for our trans - gres-sions, and
led like a lamb to the slaugh-ter, al -

bruised for our in - i - qui - ties; and to
though he was in - no-cent of crime; and cut

bring us peace he was pun-ished, and
off from the land of the liv - ing; he

by his stripes we are healed. 2. He was
paid for the guilt that was mine.

to next verse

63 Holiness is your life in me
(Only the blood)

Words and Music: Brian Doerksen

64 Holy One of God

Words and Music: Geoff Bullock

Ho - ly One of God,

the Son of Right-eous-ness,

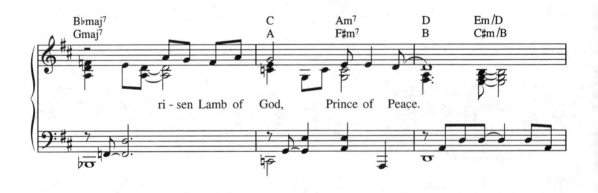

ri - sen Lamb of God, Prince of Peace.

Re - ject - ed and des - pised,

65 Hosanna

Words and Music: Carl Tuttle

1. Ho - san - na, ho - san - na, ho - san - na in the high - est! Ho - san - na, ho - san - na, ho - san - na in the high - est!
2. Glo - ry, glo - ry, glo - ry to the King of kings! Glo - ry, glo - ry, glo - ry to the King of kings!

Lord, we lift up your name, with hearts full of praise; be ex - al - ted, O Lord, my God!

Ho - san - na in the high - est!
Glo - ry to the King of Kings!

66 How can I be free from sin? *(Lead me to the cross)*

Words and Music: Graham Kendrick and Steve Thompson

1. How can I be free from sin? lead me to the cross of Je - sus, from the guilt, the pow'r, the pain, lead me to the cross of Je - sus.

There's no o - ther way, no price that I could pay,

simp - ly to the cross I cling.

This is all I need, this is all I plead,

that his blood was shed for me.

2. How can I know peace within?
   lead me to the cross of Jesus,
   sing a song of joy again,
   lead me to the cross of Jesus.

   Flowing from above,
   all-forgiving love,
   from the Father's heart to me.
   What a gift of grace,
   his own righteousness,
   clothing me in purity.

3. How can I live day by day?
   lead me to the cross of Jesus,
   following his narrow way,
   lead me to the cross of Jesus.

67 How deep the Father's love for us

Words and Music: Stuart Townend

ma - ny sons to glo - ry.

2. Behold the man upon a cross,
   my sin upon his shoulders;
   ashamed, I hear my mocking voice
   call out among the scoffers.
   It was my sin that held him there
   until it was accomplished;
   his dying breath has brought me life –
   I know that it is finished.

3. I will not boast in anything,
   no gifts, no pow'r, no wisdom;
   but I will boast in Jesus Christ,
   his death and resurrection.
   Why should I gain from his reward?
   I cannot give an answer,
   but this I know with all my heart,
   his wounds have paid my ransom.

68 How do I know you love me? *(I look to the cross)*

Words and Music: Mark Altrogge

1. How do I know you love me? I look a-round and see the sun - shine, the rain and the wind in the trees. But should these gra - cious to - kens all fade from my sight, I won't doubt your love for I fix my eyes. I look to the cross where I most clear - ly see your awe - some love dis -

2. How do I know you love me?
   At times I'm so aware.
   I sense your Holy Spirit,
   I see you ev'rywhere.
   But when I leave the mountain
   and your face is hid from sight,
   I won't doubt your love
   for I fix my eyes.

69 I believe in Jesus

Words and Music: Marc Nelson

With conviction

I
I
be-lieve in Je - sus;
be-lieve in you, Lord;

I be-lieve he is the Son of God.
I be-lieve you are the Son of God.

I be-lieve he died and rose a-gain,
I be-lieve you died and rose a-gain,

I be-lieve he paid for us all.
I be-lieve you paid for us all.

70 I know a place

(At the cross)

Words and Music: Randy and Terry Butler

I know a place, a won-der-ful place,

where ac - cused and con - demned

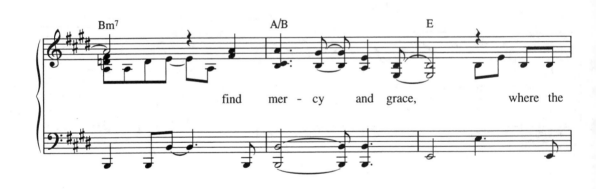

find mer - cy and grace, where the

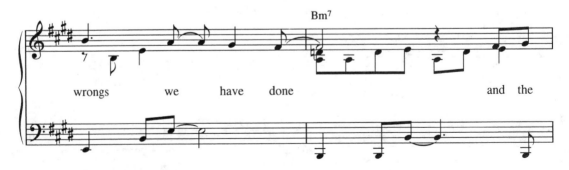

wrongs we have done and the

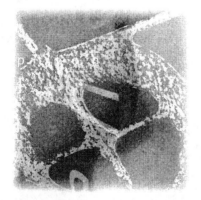

71 I know that my Redeemer lives

Words: Charles Wesley

Music: Thomas Clark
harm. Martin Shaw

CREDITON CM

1. I know that my Re - deem - er lives, and e - ver prays for me; a to - ken of his love he gives, a pledge of li - ber - ty.

2. I find him lifting up my head,
   he brings salvation near,
   his presence makes me free indeed,
   and he will soon appear.

3. He wills that I should holy be;
   what can withstand his will?
   The counsel of his grace in me
   he surely shall fulfil.

4. Jesus, I hang upon thy word;
   I steadfastly believe
   thou wilt return and claim me, Lord,
   and to thyself receive.

5. Thy love I soon expect to find
   in all its depth and height,
   to comprehend th'eternal mind,
   and grasp the Infinite.

6. When God is mine, and I am his,
   of paradise possessed,
   I taste unutterable bliss
   and everlasting rest.

72 I'm special

Words and Music: Graham Kendrick

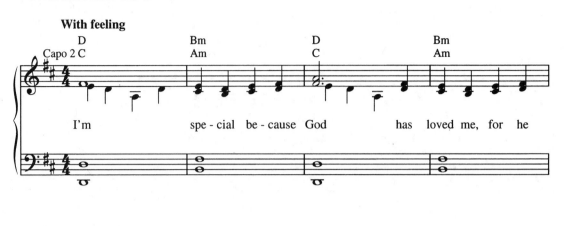

I'm spe-cial be-cause God has loved me, for he

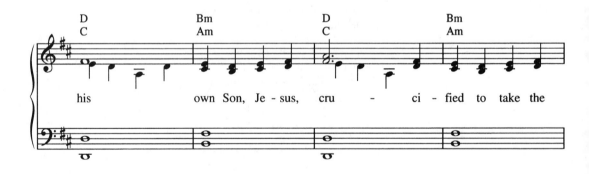

gave the best thing that he had to save me;

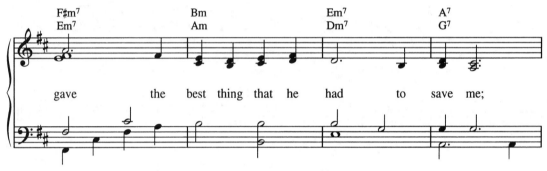

his own Son, Je - sus, cru - ci - fied to take the

blame, for all the bad things I have done.

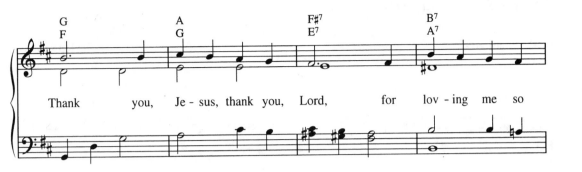

Thank you, Je - sus, thank you, Lord, for lov - ing me so

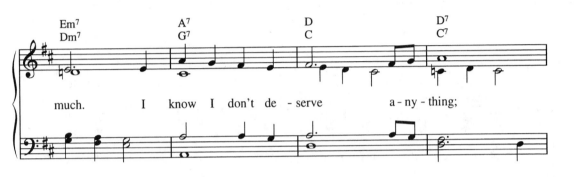

much. I know I don't de - serve a - ny - thing;

help me feel your love right now to know deep in my

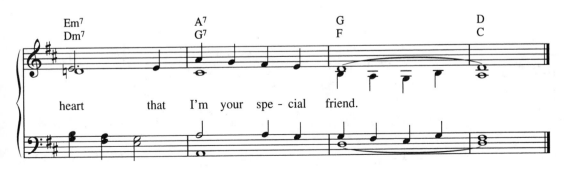

heart that I'm your spe - cial friend.

73 In Christ alone

Words: Stuart Townend

Music: Keith Getty

1. In Christ a - lone my hope is found, he is my

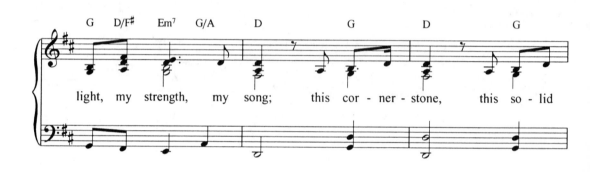

light, my strength, my song; this cor - ner - stone, this so - lid

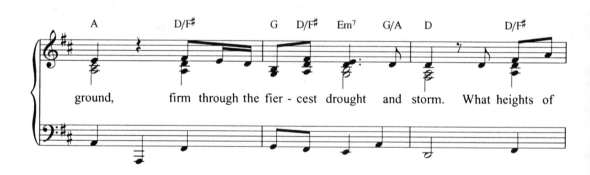

ground, firm through the fier - cest drought and storm. What heights of

love, what depths of peace, when fears are stilled, when striv - ings

cease! My com - for - ter, my all in all, here in the

love of Christ I stand.

2. In Christ alone! – who took on flesh,
   fullness of God in helpless babe!
   This gift of love and righteousness,
   scorned by the ones he came to save:
   till on that cross as Jesus died,
   the wrath of God was satisfied
   for ev'ry sin on him was laid:
   here in the death of Christ I live.

3. There in the ground his body lay,
   Light of the world by darkness slain:
   then bursting forth in glorious day
   up from the grave he rose again!
   And as he stands in victory
   sin's curse has lost its grip on me,
   for I am his and he is mine –
   bought with the precious blood of Christ.

4. No guilt in life, no fear in death,
   this is the pow'r of Christ in me;
   from life's first cry to final breath,
   Jesus commands my destiny.
   No pow'r of hell, no scheme of man,
   can ever pluck me from his hand;
   till he returns or calls me home,
   here in the pow'r of Christ I'll stand!

74 In the tomb so cold

(Christ is risen!)

Words and Music: Graham Kendrick

Triumphantly

1. In the tomb so cold they laid him, death its vic - tim

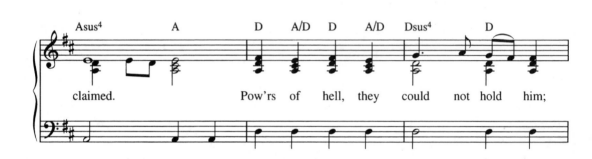

claimed. Pow'rs of hell, they could not hold him;

back to life he came! *Chorus*

(Men) Christ is ri - sen!

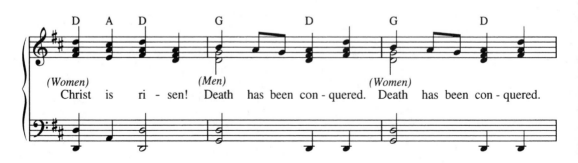

(Women) Christ is ri - sen! (Men) Death has been con - quered. (Women) Death has been con - quered.

(Men) Christ is ri - sen! (Women) Christ is ri - sen! (All) He shall reign for

e - ver.

2. Hell had spent its fury on him,
   left him crucified.
   Yet, by blood, he boldly conquered,
   sin and death defied.

3. Now the fear of death is broken,
   love has won the crown.
   Pris'ners of the darkness listen,
   walls are tumbling down.

4. Raised from death to heav'n ascending,
   love's exalted King.
   Let his song of joy, unending,
   through the nations ring!

   (Chorus twice to end)

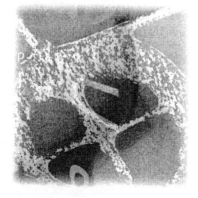

75 I stand amazed in the presence

Words and Music: Charles H. Gabriel

2. For me it was in the garden
   he prayed – 'Not my will, but thine';
   he had no tears for his own griefs,
   but sweat drops of blood for mine,

3. In pity angels beheld him,
   and came from the world of light,
   to comfort him in the sorrows
   he bore for my soul that night.

4. He took my sins and my sorrows,
   he made them his very own;
   he bore the burden to Calvary,
   and suffered, and died alone.

5. When with the ransomed in glory
   his face I at last shall see,
   'twill be my joy through the ages
   to sing of his love for me.

76 I thank you for the precious blood
(Thank you for the blood)

Words: Colin Dye and Richard Lewis
(revised and adapted by Richard Lewis)

Music: Richard Lewis

1. I thank you for the pre-cious blood of Je - sus as of a
thank you that the blood is e - ver cleans-ing me from ev - 'ry

Lamb with - out blem - ish or stain. I
sin, whe - ther thought, word or deed. Now

thank you that the blood pleads for me all the
e - vil has no hold on me, I'm re -

mer - cy and pro-vis - ions of your grace. And I
deemed by the Lamb of vic - to - ry. And I

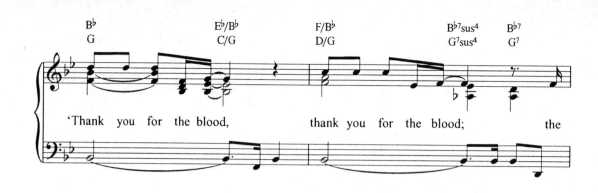

'Thank you for the blood, thank you for the blood; the

blood that gives me free - dom, the blood that gives me life.' I say

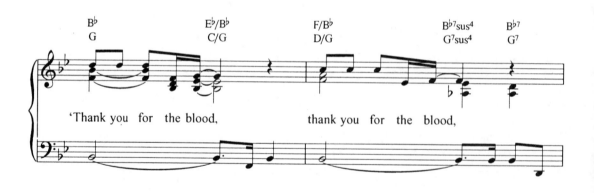

'Thank you for the blood, thank you for the blood,

thank you for the blood you shed for me.' 2. I me.'

77 It is a thing most wonderful

Words: William Walsham How

Music: Thomas Bishop Southgate

BROOKFIELD LM

1. It is a thing most won - der - ful, al - most too won - der - ful to be, that God's own Son should come from heav'n, and die to save a child like me.

2. And yet I know that it is true:
   he chose a poor and humble lot,
   and wept and toiled, and mourned and died,
   for love of those who loved him not.

3. I sometimes think about the cross,
   and shut my eyes, and try to see
   the cruel nails and crown of thorns,
   and Jesus crucified for me.

4. But even could I see him die,
   I could but see a little part
   of that great love which, like a fire,
   is always burning in his heart.

5. I cannot tell how he could love
   a child so weak and full of sin;
   his love must be most wonderful,
   if he could die my love to win.

6. It is most wonderful to know
   his love for me so free and sure;
   but 'tis more wonderful to see
   my love for him so faint and poor.

7. And yet I want to love thee, Lord;
   O light the flame within my heart,
   and I will love thee more and more,
   until I see thee as thou art.

78 It's your blood

Words and Music: Michael Christ

Steadily

It's your blood that clean - ses me, it's your blood that gives me life, it's your blood that took my place in re - deem - ing sac - ri - fice, and wash - es me whi - ter than the snow, than the snow. My Je - sus, God's pre - cious sac - ri - fice.

79 I will love you for the cross

(For the cross)

Words and Music: Matt and Beth Redman

With a strong rhythm

1. I will love you for the cross,
and I will love you for the cost:
man of suf - fer - ings, bring - er of my peace,
blood that brought me home.

You came in - to a world of shame,
and paid the price we could not pay:
death that brought me life, blood that brought me home.

2. Je - sus Christ, the sin - ner's friend;
does this kind - ness know no bounds?
With your pre - cious blood you have pur - chased me.

O the my - st'ry of the cross,
you were pun - ished, you were crushed;
but that pun - ish - ment has be - come my peace,

80 I will offer up my life

(This thankful heart)

Words and Music: Matt Redman

Gently

1. I will of-fer up my life in spi-rit and truth,

pour-ing out the oil of love as my wor-ship to you.

In sur-ren-der I must give my ev-'ry part;

Lord, re-ceive the sac-ri-fice of a bro-ken heart.

Chorus Je-sus, what can I give, what can I bring to so faith-ful a friend,

2. You deserve my ev'ry breath
   for you've paid the great cost;
   giving up your life to death,
   even death on a cross.
   You took all my shame away,
   there defeated my sin,
   opened up the gates of heav'n,
   and have beckoned me in.

81 Jesus Christ

(Once again)

Words and Music: Matt Redman

Thoughtfully, not too fast

1. Je-sus Christ, I think up-on your sac-ri-fice; you be-came no-thing, poured out to death. Ma-ny times I've won-dered at your gift of life, and I'm in that place once a-gain, I'm in that place once a-gain.

Chorus And once a-gain I look up-on the

2. Now you are exalted to the highest place,
   King of the heavens, where one day I'll bow.
   But for now I marvel at this saving grace,
   and I'm full of praise once again,
   I'm full of praise once again.

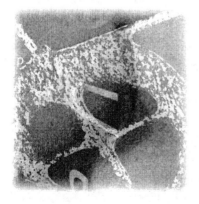

82 Jesus Christ is risen today

Words and Music: from *Lyra Davidica*

EASTER HYMN 77 77 and Alleluias

1. Je - sus Christ is ris'n to - day, al - le - lu - ia!
our tri - um - phant ho - ly day, al - le - lu - ia!
who did once, up - on the cross, al - le - lu - ia!
suf - fer to re - deem our loss, al - le - lu - ia!

2. Hymns of praise then let us sing, alleluia!
unto Christ, our heav'nly King, alleluia!
who endured the cross and grave, alleluia!
sinners to redeem and save, alleluia!

3. But the pains that he endured, alleluia!
our salvation have procured; alleluia!
now above the sky he's King, alleluia!
where the angels ever sing, alleluia!

83 Jesus Christ, you are the Son of God *(On my knees)*

Words and Music: Andy Pressdee and Ian Mizen
arr. Richard Lewis

1. Je - sus Christ, you are the Son of God, Ho -
2. You o - beyed God's plan to the ve - ry end, Ho -

- ly One, you gave ev - 'ry - thing to be - come
- ly One, be - came the sac - ri - fice that would show

like one of us. Hea - ven's Son
us the Fa - ther's love. You came to die

came to earth,
to give us life,

One day all the world will see you, one day all the world will see all cre - a - tion kneel be - fore you, all cre - a - tion sing.

Last time

84 Jesus is Lord!

Words and Music: David Mansell

With majesty

1. Je - sus is Lord! cre - a - tion's voice pro-claims it, for by his pow'r each tree and flow'r was planned and made. Je - sus is Lord! the u - ni-verse de - clares it, sun, moon and stars in hea - ven cry, 'Je - sus is Lord!'

Chorus

Je - sus is Lord! Je - sus is Lord! Praise him with hal - le - lu - jahs for Je - sus is Lord.

2. Jesus is Lord! yet from his throne eternal
in flesh he came to die in pain
on Calv'ry's tree.
Jesus is Lord! from him all life proceeding,
yet gave his life a ransom
thus setting us free.

3. Jesus is Lord! o'er sin the mighty conqueror,
from death he rose, and all his foes
shall own his name.
Jesus is Lord! God sent his Holy Spirit
to show by works of power
that Jesus is Lord.

85 Jesus isn't dead any more

Words and Music: Capt. Alan Price, CA

2. He went back to be with God,
but we know he's still near;
Jesus sent the Spirit of God,
and he is always here with us.

86 Jesus, King of the ages *(Prophet, Priest and King)*

Words and Music: David Lyle Morris and Faith Forster

Moderately

Chorus

Je - sus, King of the a - ges, plead-ing our cause be - fore the throne of God. Je - sus, the liv-ing Word of God, our Pro-phet, Priest and King, our Pro-phet, Priest and King.

3rd time to Bridge

Fine

(last time)

87 Jesus, life giver

Words and Music: Sue Howson arr. Donald Thomson

2. I come to you
   to bow my knee.
   You are my Lord and King,

88 Jesus lives! thy terrors now

Words: Christian Fürchtegott Gellert
trans. Frances Elizabeth Cox, alt.

Music: Henry John Gauntlett

ST ALBINUS 78 78 and Alleluia

1. Je - sus lives! thy ter - rors now can no more, O

death, ap - pal us; Je - sus lives! by this we know

thou, O grave, canst not en - thral us. Al - le - lu - ia.

2. Jesus lives! henceforth is death
   but the gate of life immortal:
   this shall calm our trembling breath,
   when we pass its gloomy portal.
   Alleluia.

3. Jesus lives! for us he died;
   then, alone to Jesus living,
   pure in heart may we abide,
   glory to our Saviour giving.
   Alleluia.

4. Jesus lives! our hearts know well
   naught from us his love shall sever;
   life nor death nor pow'rs of hell
   tear us from his keeping ever.
   Alleluia.

5. Jesus lives! to him the throne
   over all the world is given:
   may we go where he is gone,
   rest and reign with him in heaven.
   Alleluia.

89 Jesus, Prince and Saviour

Words: Timothy Dudley-Smith

Music: Arthur Seymour Sullivan

ST GERTRUDE 65 65 D and Refrain

1. Je - sus, Prince and Sa - viour, Lord of life who died;

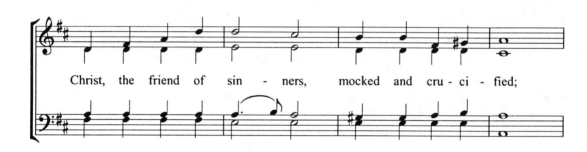

Christ, the friend of sin - ners, mocked and cru - ci - fied;

for a world's sal - va - tion, he his bo - dy gave,

lay at last death's vic - tim, life - less in the grave.

Chorus

Lord of life tri - um - phant, ri - sen now to reign! King of

King of end - less a - ges,
end - less a - ges, Je - sus lives a - gain!

2. In his pow'r and Godhead
   ev'ry vict'ry won;
   pain and passion ended,
   all his purpose done.
   Christ the Lord is risen!
   sighs and sorrows past,
   death's dark night is over,
   morning comes at last!

3. Resurrection morning!
   sinners' bondage freed;
   Christ the Lord is risen —
   he is ris'n indeed!
   Jesus, Prince and Saviour,
   Lord of Life who died,
   Christ the King of Glory
   now is glorified!

90 Jesus, thank you for the cross

Words and Music: Mike Burn
arr. Donald Thomson

91 Jesus, the broken bread

Words: Nick Fawcett

Music: Noel Rawsthorne

HESWALL 10 10 10 10

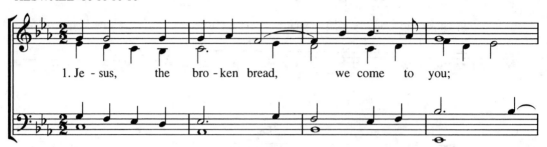

1. Je - sus, the bro - ken bread, we come to you;

emp - ty, we would be fed – meet us a - new.

Teach us to hun - ger af - ter right - eous - ness,

reach out in love, we pray, to guide and bless.

2. Jesus, poured out wine, we come with awe;
   thirsty, we take the cup – quench and restore.
   Teach us to seek your kingdom and your will,
   reach out in love, we pray, our lives to fill.

3. Jesus, the crucified, we come with shame;
   greedy, we've sought reward – made that our aim.
   Teach us to worship now through word and deed,
   reach out in love, we pray, to all in need.

4. Jesus, the risen Lord, we come with praise;
   gladly, we sing of you, our hearts ablaze.
   Teach us to glimpse new life beyond the grave,
   reach out in love, we pray, to heal and save.

5. Jesus, the living one, we come with joy,
   truly, no evil can your love destroy.
   Teach us to walk in faith, though hope seems vain,
   reach out in love, we pray, renew again.

6. Jesus, the King of kings, we come to serve,
   freely give all for you as you deserve.
   Teach us to share the love you daily show,
   reach out in love, we pray, and bid us go.

92 Jesus, the Holy One

Words and Music: Susie Hare

Unhurried

1. Je - sus, the Ho - ly One, the pre - cious gift of God's own Son. Je - sus, the Ho - ly One, we bow be - fore you now.

Chorus

We bow down, we bow down, we bow down, we bow down, be -

fore you. We bow down, we

bow down, we bow down be - fore you.

2. Jesus, the Holy Lamb,
   the sacrifice of God for man.
   Jesus, the Holy Lamb,
   we bow before you now.

3. Jesus, the holy name
   that takes our sin, that bears our shame.
   Jesus, the holy name,
   we bow before you now.

93 Jesus, we celebrate your victory

Words and Music: John Gibson

2. His Spirit in us releases us from fear,
   the way to him is open, with boldness we draw near.
   And in his presence our problems disappear;
   our hearts responding to his love.

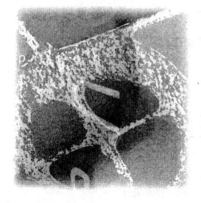

94 Jesus, you're the morning star

Words: Mike Burn

Music: Traditional

Je - sus, you're the morn - ing star, Oh how beau - ti -

ful you are. You came down from hea - ven a - bove,

died to show the Fa - ther's love. Je - sus, you're the

morn - ing star, Oh how beau - ti - ful you are.

95 Led like a lamb

(You're alive)

Words and Music: Graham Kendrick

Thoughtfully

1. Led like a lamb to the slaugh - ter in si - lence and shame, there on your back you car - ried a world of vio - lence and pain. Bleed - ing, dy - ing bleed - ing,

Triumphantly

Gsus⁴   *Chorus*   C   Bb/C   C   Bb/C

dy - ing.   You're a - live, you're a-live, you have ri - sen,

F   C   F   C   F   C   Dm   F/G   C   Bb/C   C   Bb/C

*al - le - lu - ia! (al - le - lu - ia!) (al - le - lu - ia!) And the pow'r and the glo - ry is gi - ven,

F   C   F   C   F   C   Dm   F/G   C   Bb/C   F   C

1st and 2nd times

al - le - lu - ia! (al - le - lu - ia!) (al - le - lu - ia!) Je-sus to   you.

Last time

C   Bb/C   F   C   C   Bb/C   F   C

you.

* Optional antiphonal alleluias: the congregation divides into three parts.

2. At break of dawn, poor Mary,
   still weeping she came,
   when through her grief she heard your voice
   now speaking her name.
   (Men) (Women) (Men) (Women)
   Mary, Master, Mary, Master.

3. At the right hand of the Father
   now seated on high
   you have begun your eternal reign
   of justice and joy.
   Glory, glory, glory, glory.

96 Light of the World

Words and Music: Tim Hughes

With feeling

1. Light of the World, you stepped down in-to dark-ness,
2. King of all days oh so high-ly ex-al-ted,

o-pened my eyes, let me see beau-ty that made this
glo-rious in hea-ven a-bove. Hum-bly you came to the

heart a-dore you, hope of a life spent with you.
earth you cre-a-ted, all for love's sake be-came poor.

Chorus
So here I am to wor-ship, here I am to bow down, here I am to

say that you're my God, and you're al-to-ge-ther

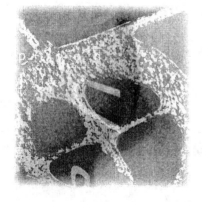

97 Look, ye saints

Words: Thomas Kelly

Music: Henry Smart

REGENT SQUARE 87 87 87

1. Look, ye saints, the sight is glo-rious: see the Man of Sor-rows now;
from the fight re-turned vic-to-rious, ev-'ry knee to him shall bow:
Crown him, crown him! Crown him, crown him! Crowns be-come the Vic-tor's brow.

2. Crown the Saviour! Angels, crown him!
Rich the trophies Jesus brings;
in the seat of pow'r enthrone him,
while the vault of heaven rings:
Crown him, crown him!
Crown him, crown him!
Crown the Saviour King of kings!

3. Sinners in derision crowned him,
mocking thus the Saviour's claim;
saints and angels crowd around him,
own his title, praise his name:
Crown him, crown him!
Crown him, crown him!
Spread abroad the Victor's fame.

4. Hark, those bursts of acclamation!
Hark, those loud triumphant chords!
Jesus takes the highest station:
O what joy the sight affords!
Crown him, crown him!
Crown him, crown him!
King of kings and Lord of lords!

98 Lord, I lift your name on high

(You came from heaven to earth)

Words and Music: Rick Founds

Lord, I lift your name on high;

Lord, I love to sing your prai - ses.

I'm so glad you're in my life;

I'm so glad you came to save us.

You came from hea - ven to earth to show the way,

from the earth to the cross, my debt to pay,

from the cross to the grave, from the grave to the sky,

Lord, I lift your name on high.

99 Lord of the heavens

Words and Music: Shaun and Mel Griffiths
arr. Chris Mitchell

Lord of the hea - vens, I bow my knee and
wor - ship you, I stand be - fore you
and I am a - mazed, I see your beau - ty
dis - played in ev - 'ry - thing you do. For you are my Sa - viour, Lord

100 Lord, we've come to worship

Words and Music: Tommy Coombes and Don Moen
arr. Chris Mitchell

1. Lord, we've come to wor - ship, and we have come to pray;
2. Lord, we need for - give - ness, we've wan-dered far a - way;

Lord, we've come to lis - ten, and
look down in ten - der mer - cy, for-

hear what you would say; O
give our sins, we pray; O

Lord, our hearts are long - ing to meet with you to - day; for
Lord, we need re - viv - al, all a - cross this land; come

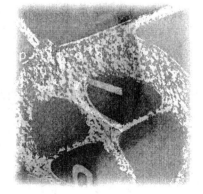

101 Lord, what a sacrifice I see   *(The greatest love)*

Words and Music: Susie Hare

1. Lord, what a sacrifice I see as I turn my eyes to Calvary; my sins nailed to a tree, a King stands in instead of me.

2. Lord, what a promise of your grace as I turn my eyes to seek your face; clothed in righteousness, I place my sinfulness in your embrace.

3. Lord, what a privilege I own to freely come before your throne; there, to know and to be known, surrendered now to you alone.

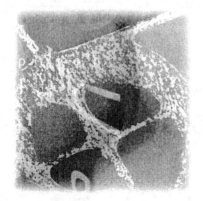

102 Love's redeeming work is done

Words: Charles Wesley

Music: John Wesley's *Foundery Collection*

SAVANNAH 77 77

1. Love's re-deem-ing work is done; fought the fight, the bat-tle won: lo, our Sun's e-clipse is o'er, lo, he sets in blood no more.

2. Vain the stone, the watch, the seal;
   Christ has burst the gates of hell;
   death in vain forbids his rise;
   Christ has opened paradise.

3. Lives again our glorious King;
   where, O death, is now thy sting?
   Dying once, he all doth save;
   where thy victory, O grave?

4. Soar we now where Christ has led,
   foll'wing our exalted Head;
   made like him, like him we rise;
   ours the cross, the grave, the skies.

5. Hail the Lord of earth and heav'n!
   praise to thee by both be giv'n;
   thee we greet triumphant now;
   hail, the Resurrection thou!

103 Low in the grave he lay

Words and Music: Robert Lowry

CHRIST AROSE 65 64 and Refrain

1. Low in the grave he lay, Je - sus, my Sa - viour; wait - ing the com - ing day, Je - sus, my Lord.

Chorus

Up from the grave he a - rose, with a migh - ty tri - umph o'er his foes; he a - rose a vic - tor from the dark do - main, and he

lives for e - ver with his saints to reign. He a - rose! He a-

rose! Hal - le - lu - jah! Christ a - rose!

2. Vainly they watch his bed,
   Jesus, my Saviour;
   vainly they seal the dead,
   Jesus, my Lord.

3. Death cannot keep its prey,
   Jesus, my Saviour;
   he tore the bars away,
   Jesus, my Lord.

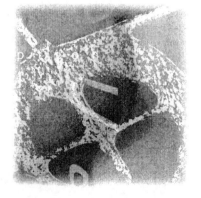

104 Man of sorrows

Words and Music: Philipp Bliss, alt.

GETHSEMANE 777 8

1. Man of sor-rows! What a name for the Son of God who came ru-ined sin-ners to re-claim! Al-le-lu - ia! What a Sa-viour!

2. Bearing shame and scoffing rude,
   in my place condemned he stood;
   sealed my pardon with his blood:
   Alleluia! What a Saviour!

3. Guilty, vile and helpless we;
   spotless Lamb of God was he:
   full atonement – can it be?
   Alleluia! What a Saviour!

4. Lifted up was he to die:
   'It is finished!' was his cry;
   now in heav'n exalted high:
   Alleluia! What a Saviour!

5. When he comes, our glorious King,
   all his ransomed home to bring,
   then anew this song we'll sing:
   Alleluia! What a Saviour!

105 Meekness and majesty

(This is your God)

Words and Music: Graham Kendrick

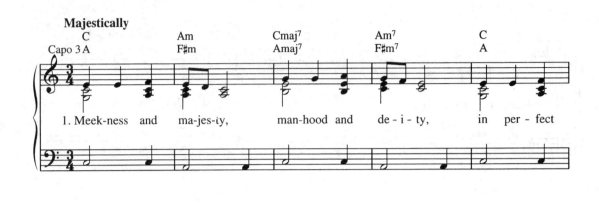

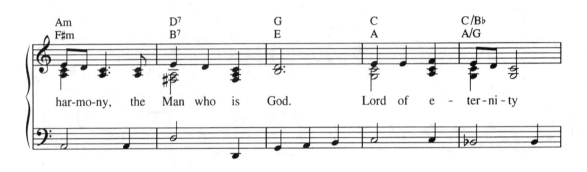

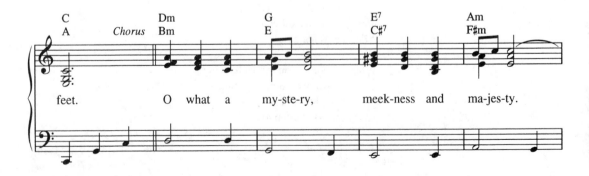

2. Father's pure radiance,
   perfect in innocence,
   yet learns obedience
   to death on a cross.
   Suffering to give us life,
   conquering through sacrifice,
   and as they crucify
   prays: 'Father forgive.'

3. Wisdom unsearchable,
   God the invisible,
   love indestructible
   in frailty appears.
   Lord of infinity,
   stooping so tenderly,
   lifts our humanity
   to the heights of his throne.

106 Most holy judge

(I'm justified)

Words and Music: Steve and Vikki Cook

1. Most ho-ly judge, I stood be-fore you guil-ty, when you sent Je-sus to the cross for my sin. There your love was re-vealed, your jus-tice vin-di-ca-ted. One sac-ri-fice has paid the cost for all

2. I come to you and I can call you 'Father',
   there is no fear, there is no shame before you.
   For by your gift of grace now I am one of your children,
   an heir with those who bear your name and share the hope of glory.

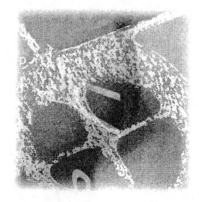

107 My Lord loves me

Words: Carole Pegler

Music: Traditional
arr. E.J. Hume

Chorus

My Lord loves me and oh, the
died for me, on a cross at

won-der I see! A rain-bow shines in my
Cal-va-ry, he bore my sin and my

win-dow: my Lord loves me.
shame when he died for me.

Verse
He

108 My Lord, what love is this

(Amazing love)

Words and Music: Graham Kendrick

1. My Lord, what love is this, that pays so dear - ly, that I, the guil - ty one, may go free!

A - maz - ing love, O what sac - ri - fice, the

2. And so they watched him die,
   despised, rejected;
   but O, the blood he shed
   flowed for me!

3. And now this love of Christ
   shall flow like rivers;
   come, wash your guilt away,
   live again!

109 My song is love unknown

Words: Samuel Crossman

Music: John Ireland

LOVE UNKNOWN 66 66 88

1. My song is love un - known, my Sa-viour's love to me; love to the love - less shown, that they might love - ly be. O who am I, that for my sake my Lord should take frail flesh and die?

2. He came from his blest throne
   salvation to bestow;
   but men made strange, and none
   the longed-for Christ would know:
   but O, my friend,
   my friend indeed,
   who at my need
   his life did spend.

3. Sometimes they strew his way,
   and his sweet praises sing;
   resounding all the day
   hosannas to their King:
   then 'Crucify!'
   is all their breath,
   and for his death
   they thirst and cry.

4. They rise and needs will have,
   my dear Lord made away;
   a murderer they save,
   the Prince of Life they slay;
   yet cheerful he
   to suff'ring goes,
   that he his foes
   from thence might free.

5. Here might I stay and sing,
   no story so divine;
   never was love, dear King!
   Never was grief like thine.
   This is my friend,
   in whose sweet praise
   I all my days
   could gladly spend.

110 Name of all majesty

Words: Timothy Dudley-Smith

Music: Malcolm Archer

NAME OF ALL MAJESTY 66 64 D

1. Name of all majesty, fa-thom-less mys-te-ry, King of the a-ges by an-gels a-dored; pow'r and au-tho-ri-ty, splen-dour and dig-ni-ty, bow to his mas-te-ry, Je-sus is Lord!

2. Child of our destiny,
God from eternity,
love of the Father
on sinners outpoured;
see now what God has done
sending his only Son,
Christ the beloved one,
Jesus is Lord!

3. Saviour of Calvary,
costliest victory,
darkness defeated
and Eden restored;
born as a man to die,
nailed to a cross on high,
cold in the grave to lie,
Jesus is Lord!

4. Source of all sovereignty,
light, immortality,
life everlasting
and heaven assured;
so with the ransomed, we
praise him eternally,
Christ in his majesty,
Jesus is Lord!

111 No scenes of stately majesty

Words and Music: Graham Kendrick

1. No scenes of state-ly ma-jes-ty for the King of kings. No nights a-glow with can-dle flame for the King of love. No flags of em-pire hung in shame for Cal-va-ry. No flow'rs per-fumed the lone-ly way

that led him to   a bor-rowed tomb for Eas-ter

day.

2. No wreaths upon the ground were laid
   for the King of kings.
   only a crown of thorns remained
   where he gave his love.
   A message scrawled in irony –
   King of the Jews –
   lay trampled where they turned away,
   and no-one knew
   that it was the first Easter Day.

3. Yet nature's finest colours blaze
   for the King of kings.
   And stars in jewelled clusters say,
   'Worship heaven's King.'
   Two thousand springtimes more have bloomed –
   is that enough?
   Oh, how can I be satisfied
   until he hears
   the whole world sing of Easter love.

4. My prayers shall be a fragrance sweet
   for the King of kings.
   My love the flowers at his feet
   for the King of love.
   My vigil is to watch and pray
   until he comes.
   My highest tribute to obey
   and live to know
   the power of that first Easter Day.

5. I long for scenes of majesty
   for the risen King.
   or nights aglow with candle flame
   for the King of love.
   A nation hushed upon its knees
   at Calvary,
   where all our sins and griefs were nailed
   and hope was born
   of everlasting Easter Day.

112 O God, Most High *(You have broken the chains)*

Words and Music: Jamie Owens-Collins

113 Oh, lead me

Words and Music: Martin Smith

Oh, lead me to the place where I can

find you, oh, lead me

to the place where you'll be.

Lead me to the cross where we first met,

114 On a cross he died

(Tomb breaker)

Words and Music: Jennifer Reay
arr. Chris Mitchell

On a cross he died, he was cru-ci-fied. He did it for us, he did it for us. But that's not the end of the sto - ry; he was strong-er than death. That's not the end of the sto - ry; for

115 On a hill far away

(The old rugged cross)

Words and Music: George Bennard

THE OLD RUGGED CROSS Irregular and Refrain

1. On a hill far a - way stood an old rug-ged cross, the em - blem of suff - 'ring and shame; and I loved that old cross where the dear - est and best for a world of lost sin - ners was slain. *Chorus* So I'll cher - ish the old rug - ged cross, till my tro - phies at last I lay down;

I will cling to the old rug - ged cross

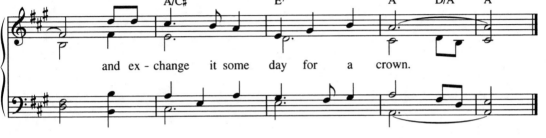

and ex - change it some day for a crown.

2. O, that old rugged cross, so despised by the world,
   has a wondrous attraction for me:
   for the dear Lamb of God left his glory above
   to bear it to dark Calvary.

3. In the old rugged cross, stained with blood so divine,
   a wondrous beauty I see.
   for 'twas on that old cross Jesus suffered and died
   to pardon and sanctify me.

4. To the old rugged cross I will ever be true,
   its shame and reproach gladly bear.
   Then he'll call me some day to my home far away;
   there his glory for ever I'll share.

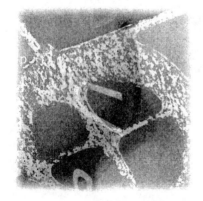

116 On Calvary's tree

Words: A.W. Edsor

Music: A.E. Walton adapted by A.W. Edsor

117 On the blood-stained ground *(I kneel down)*

Words and Music: Graham Kendrick

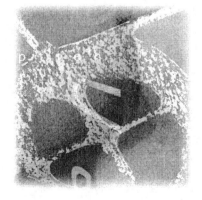

118 On the cross

Words and Music: Geoff Baker

1. On the cross, on the cross, where the King of Glo-ry died, here is grace, here is love, flow-ing from that wound-ed side. A-maz-ing mys-te-ry, that he should die for me, as a

2. At the cross, at the cross,
   all my sin on Jesus laid.
   Mine the debt, his the cost,
   by his blood the price is paid.
   And through his suffering,
   that fragrant offering,
   arms of love are opened wide.
   At the cross, at the cross,
   there is healing at the cross.

   To the cross, to the cross,
   Spirit lead me to the cross.
   Bowed in awe at his feet,
   richest gain I count as loss.
   Nothing compares with this,
   to share his righteousness
   and be called a child of God.
   To the cross, to the cross,
   Spirit lead me to the cross.

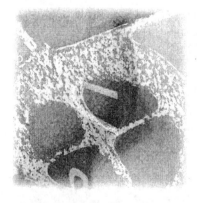

119 On this day, the first of days

Words: 18th century
trans. Henry Williams Baker
adapted by the editors of *English Praise*

Music: Freylinghausen's *Gesangbuch*

LÜBECK (GOTT SEI DANK) 77 77

1. On this day, the first of days, God the Fa-ther's name we praise,
who, cre - a - tion's Lord and spring, did the world from dark - ness bring.

2. On this day his only Son
   over death the triumph won;
   on this day the Spirit came
   with his gifts of living flame.

3. On this day his people raise
   one pure sacrifice of praise,
   and, with all the saints above,
   tell of Christ's redeeming love.

4. Praise, O God, to thee be giv'n,
   praise on earth and praise in heav'n,
   praise to thy eternal Son,
   who this day our vict'ry won.

120 O sacred head, once wounded

Words: Paulus Gerhardt attrib. Bernard of Clairvaux
trans. James Waddell Alexander

Music: Melody by Hans Leo Hassler
arr. Johann Sebastian Bach

PASSION CHORALE 76 76 D

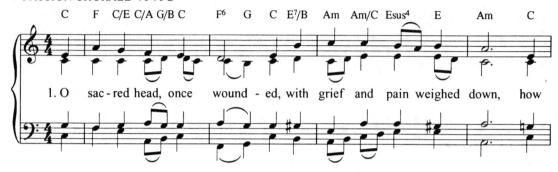

1. O sac - red head, once wound - ed, with grief and pain weighed down, how

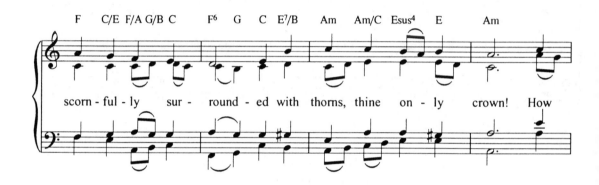

scorn - ful - ly sur - round - ed with thorns, thine on - ly crown! How

pale art thou with an - guish, with sore a - buse and scorn! How

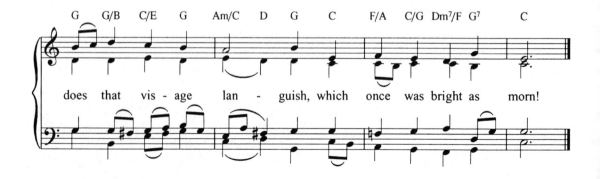

does that vis - age lan - guish, which once was bright as morn!

2. O Lord of life and glory,
   what bliss till now was thine!
   I read the wondrous story,
   I joy to call thee mine.
   Thy grief and thy compassion
   were all for sinners' gain;
   mine, mine was the transgression,
   but thine the deadly pain.

3. What language shall I borrow
   to praise thee, heav'nly friend,
   for this, thy dying sorrow,
   thy pity without end?
   Lord, make me thine for ever,
   nor let me faithless prove;
   O let me never, never
   abuse such dying love!

4. Be near me, Lord, when dying;
   O show thyself to me;
   and for my succour flying,
   come, Lord, to set me free:
   these eyes, new faith receiving,
   from Jesus shall not move;
   for he who dies believing,
   dies safely through thy love.

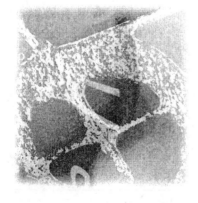

121 O the blood of Jesus

Words and Music: Unknown

122 O the passion

Words and Music: Dave Baroni and Gary Sadler

With a Celtic feel

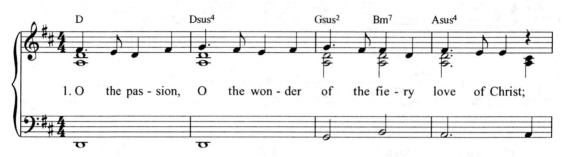

1. O the pas - sion, O the won - der of the fie - ry love of Christ;

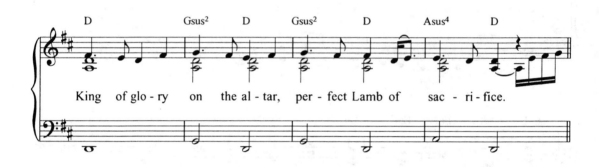

King of glo - ry on the al - tar, per - fect Lamb of sac - ri - fice.

Chorus

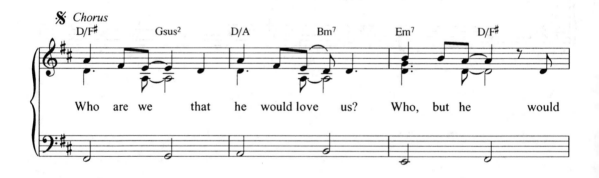

Who are we that he would love us? Who, but he would

give his life? O the pas - sion,

O the won-der of the fie-ry love of Christ.

2. O the wisdom, O the wonder
of the power of the cross;
love so rare no words could tell it,
life himself has died for us.

Who are we that he would save us?
Crucified to give us life;
O the wisdom, O the wonder
of the power of the cross.

3. O the passion, O the wonder
of the fiery love of Christ;
death defeated by his rising,
darkness conquered by his light.

We will sing his praise for ever,
worthy is the Lamb of Life;
O the passion, O the wonder
of the fiery love of Christ.

Who are we that he would love us?
Who, but he would give his life?
O the passion, O the wonder
of the fiery love of Christ.

123 O, what a morning

(Christ is risen)

Words and Music: Graham Kendrick

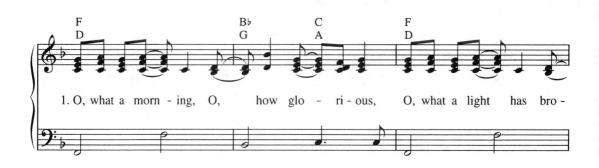

1. O, what a morn-ing, O, how glo-ri-ous, O, what a light has bro-

-ken through! Out of the tomb of death and dark des-pair,

an-gels in white an-nounce in-cre-di-ble news.

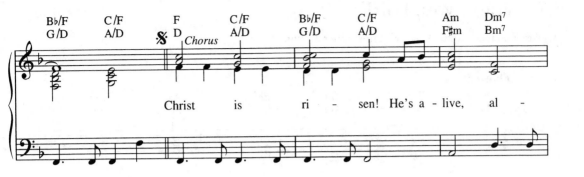

Christ is ri - sen! He's a - live, al -

le - lu - ia! Yes, he's ri - sen, he's a - live, al -

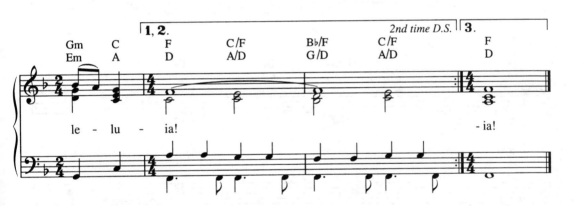

1, 2.   *2nd time D.S.*   **3.**

le - lu - ia!   - ia!

2. Suddenly hope has filled our darkest night,
   suddenly life has blossomed here;
   suddenly joy has rushed like rivers,
   he is alive and love has conquered our fear.

124 Praise you, Lord

Words and Music: Nettie Rose arr. Christopher Norton

praise you, Lord, for your love for me.

2. Praise you, Lord,
   for your gift of liberation;
   praise you, Lord,
   you have set the captives free;
   the chains that bind are broken
   by the sharpness of your sword –
   praise you, Lord,
   you gave your life for me.

3. Praise you, Lord,
   you have borne the depths of sorrow;
   praise you, Lord,
   for your anguish on the tree;
   the nails that tore your body
   and the pain that tore your soul –
   praise you, Lord,
   your tears, they fell for me.

4. Praise you, Lord,
   you have turned our thorns to roses;
   glory, Lord, as they bloom upon your brow;
   the path of pain is hallowed,
   for your love has made it sweet –
   praise you, Lord,
   and may I love you now.

125 Risen!

Words and Music: Mark and Helen Johnson

Punchy and positive

Chorus

Ri - sen! Ri - sen! Je - sus is ri - sen! The

Spi - rit was gi - ven, Je - sus is a - live!

last time to Coda

1. Ear - ly in the morn - ing, on the first day of the week,

wo - men went to vi - sit at the tomb;

an-gels came and told them: 'The one you've come to see,

he is-n't here, but you will meet him soon!'

CODA

Ri - sen! Ri - sen! Je - sus is ri - sen!

2. Fearful and excited, amazed by all they'd seen,
   Mary and her friends ran from the tomb:
   finding the disciples together where they'd meet,
   bursting with joy, they ran into the room.

3. Two of the believers, with thoughts about the week,
   walked the road so lonely and confused.
   While they spoke of Jesus, and all he'd come to mean,
   he came along beside them with the news.

4. All of his disciples were terrified to see
   Jesus before them in the room.
   'Why are you so frightened?' he said 'It's really me!
   all of the things I told you have come true!'

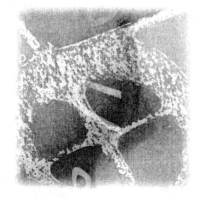

126 Rock of ages

Words: Augustus Montague Toplady, alt.

Music: Richard Redhead

PETRA (REDHEAD NO. 76) 77 77 77

1. Rock of a-ges, cleft for me, let me hide my-self in thee;
let the wa-ter and the blood, from thy ri-ven side which flowed,
be of sin the dou-ble cure: cleanse me from its guilt and pow'r.

2. Not the labours of my hands
can fulfil thy law's demands;
could my zeal no respite know,
could my tears for ever flow,
all for sin could not atone:
thou must save, and thou alone.

3. Nothing in my hands I bring,
simply to the cross I cling;
naked, come to thee for dress;
helpless, look to thee for grace;
tainted, to the fountain fly;
wash me, Saviour, or I die.

4. While I draw this fleeting breath,
when mine eyelids close in death,
when I soar through tracts unknown,
see thee on thy judgement throne;
Rock of ages, cleft for me,
let me hide myself in thee.

127 Saviour, I will sing to you *(Saviour of the world)*

Words and Music: Tim Lomax
arr. Richard Lewis

1. Sa-viour, I will sing to you a heart-felt song of love for
2. Je-sus, now you reach the lost in the sha-dow of the

you, and ev-'ry day I'll give my life
cross. It's there they taste your grace so sweet,

in wor-ship as a sac-ri-fice. You gave your all to set me
and there that love and jus-tice meet. You took the sting of death a-

free by dy-ing on the cross for me.
way and now we live in vic-to-ry.

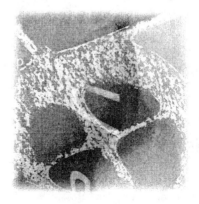

128 See the love of God poured out
(Look to the cross)

Words and Music: Mike Burn

See the love of God poured out, look to the cross,

gaze up-on the one we pierced, look to the cross.

See him taste the bit-ter wine, look to the cross,

'It is fin-ished' was his cry, look to the cross.

Chorus

Look to the cross, there the King of Love was

lift-ed up   for all the world to see.   Look   to the blood

flow-ing from his side,   it's pow'r re-leased for all e-ter-ni-ty.

On-ly   one man,   on-ly   one God could lay down his life   for

me,   Je   -   sus.

2. Know your sin that caused his pain,
   kneel at the cross,
   ask forgiveness in his name,
   kneel at the cross.
   Wonder at the price he paid,
   kneel at the cross,
   all your guilt is washed away,
   kneel at the cross.

3. Die to self to rise with him,
   share in the cross,
   glory's won through suffering,
   share in the cross.
   Joy before him, Christ endured,
   share in the cross,
   lives redeemed his great reward,
   share in the cross.

129 Should he who made the stars

(We sing your mercies)

Words and Music: Mark Altrogge

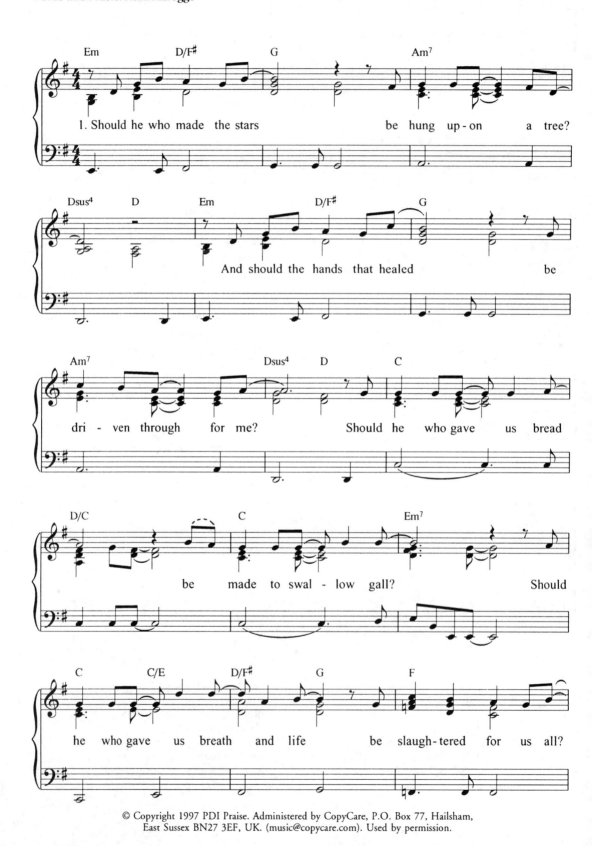

1. Should he who made the stars be hung up-on a tree? And should the hands that healed be dri-ven through for me? Should he who gave us bread be made to swal-low gall? Should he who gave us breath and life be slaugh-tered for us all?

2. Should he who is the light be cast into the dark?
   And should the Lord of love be pierced through his own heart?
   Should he who called us friends be deserted by us all?
   Should he who lived a sinless life be punished for our fall?

130 Sing out an Easter song

Words and Music: Mark and Helen Johnson
arr. Dave Bankhead

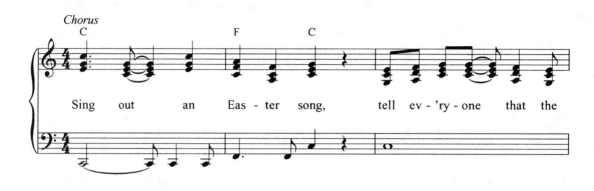

Chorus

Sing out an Eas-ter song, tell ev-'ry-one that the

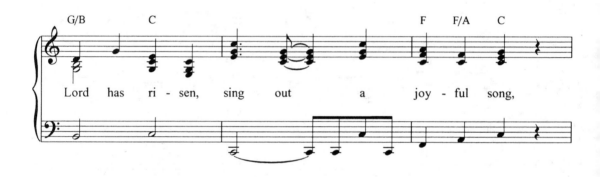

Lord has ri-sen, sing out a joy-ful song,

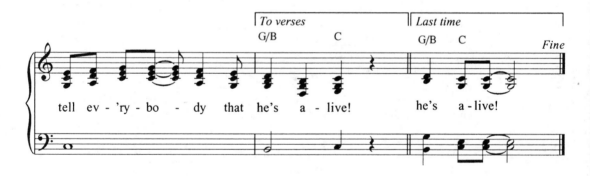

To verses

tell ev-'ry-bo — dy that he's a-live!

Last time

he's a-live!

1. Je-sus Christ, Son of God, gave his life up -

on a cross, but the pow'r of death was not e-

nough to hold him down.

2. Taken down from public view,
   he was placed inside a tomb,
   but the pow'r of love broke through
   and raised him back to life.

3. He returned to see his friends,
   showed himself alive again.
   What a day it must have been
   to have him back again!

131 Son of Man

Words and Music: David Bird and Sarah Lacy
arr. Chris Mitchell

Son of Man, led to die on a cross, nailed and bleed-ing, and the
life ebbed a-way, though my sins were red as scar-let, your

hea-vens dark-ened in your name. There was dust, there was heat, there was
blood has washed them white as snow, and a death bring-ing life, though be-

pain and there was glo-ry and ful-fil-ment of the pro-phet's words. Son of
yond my un-der-stand-ing, is made real in me if I be-lieve.

Man, you shed your blood, I could know no great-er

1. C/E   F   Gsus⁴ G   **2** C/E   F   Gsus⁴ G   Gsus⁴

love.   As   your love.   O-pen hearts will re - ceive   all the

C/E   F   C/G   G⁷sus⁴   C

joy they could i - ma -gine, and the gift of life from you,   Son of Man.

132 Such love

Words and Music: Graham Kendrick

2. Such love, stilling my restlessness;
   such love, filling my emptiness;
   such love, showing me holiness;
   O Jesus, such love.

3. Such love springs from eternity;
   such love, streaming through history;
   such love, fountain of life to me;
   O Jesus, such love.

133 Take up thy cross, the Saviour said

Words: Charles William Everest
based on Mark 8, alt.

Music: *As Hymnodus Sacer*
arr. Felix Mendelssohn

BRESLAU LM

1. Take up thy cross, the Saviour said, if thou wouldst my dis-ci-ple be; de-ny thy-self, the world for-sake, and hum-bly fol-low af-ter me.

2. Take up thy cross – let not its weight
   fill thy weak spirit with alarm:
   his strength shall bear thy spirit up,
   and brace thy heart, and nerve thine arm.

3. Take up thy cross, nor heed the shame,
   nor let thy foolish pride rebel:
   thy Lord for thee the Cross endured,
   to save thy soul from death and hell.

4. Take up thy cross then in his strength,
   and calmly ev'ry danger brave;
   'twill guide thee to a better home,
   and lead to vict'ry o'er the grave.

5. Take up thy cross, and follow Christ,
   nor think till death to lay it down;
   for only those who bear the cross
   may hope to wear the glorious crown.

6. To thee, great Lord, the One in Three,
   all praise for evermore ascend:
   O grant us in our home to see
   the heav'nly life that knows no end.

134 Thank you for saving me

Words and Music: Martin Smith

2. Mercy and grace are mine, forgiv'n is my sin;
   Jesus, my only hope, the Saviour of the world.
   'Great is the Lord,' we cry; God, let your kingdom come.
   Your word has let me see, thank you for saving me.

135 Thank you for the cross

(O I love you, Lord)

Words and Music: Graham Kendrick

love you, Lord. I will ne - ver un - der-stand why you love
me. You're my deep - est joy, you're my
heart's de-light, and the great - est thing of all, O Lord, I
see: you de-light in me!

2. For our healing there,
   Lord, you suffered,
   and to take our fear
   you poured out your love,
   precious Lord (precious Lord).
   Calvary's work is done,
   you have conquered,
   able now to save
   so completely,
   thank you, Lord (thank you, Lord).

136 Thank you, Jesus

Words and Music: Unknown

2. You rose up from the grave,
   to me new life you gave,
   thank you, Lord, for loving me.
   You rose up from the grave,
   to me new life you gave,
   thank you, Lord, for loving me.

3. You're coming back again,
   and we with you shall reign.
   Thank you, Lord, for loving me.
   You're coming back again,
   and we with you shall reign.
   Thank you, Lord, for loving me.

137 The cross has said it all

Words and Music: Matt Redman and Martin Smith

1. The

cross has said it all,   the cross has said it all.
cross has said it all,   the cross has said it all.

I can't de - ny what you have shown,   the
I ne - ver re - cog - nised your touch,   un -

cross speaks of a God of love;   there dis-played for all
til I met you at the cross.   We are fall - en, dust

to see,   Je - sus Christ, our on - ly hope,   a
to dust,   how could you do this for us?

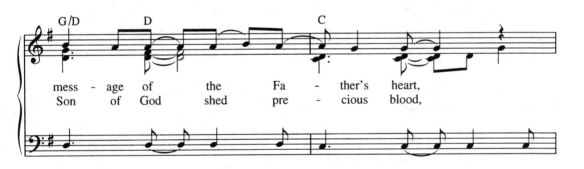

mess - age of the Fa - ther's heart,
Son of God shed pre - cious blood,

'Come, my child - ren, come on home.'   As
who can com - pre - hend this love?   As

138 The darkest hour, Lord Jesus

Words: G.R. Cowell
adapted Graham Kendrick

Music: Melody by Hans Leo Hassler
harm. Johann Sebastian Bach

2. What perfect, meek submission! Your will, not mine be done.
   Obedience full, unquestioned; perfection of a Son!
   Thus prostrate there before him, your sweat as drops of blood
   and so to be the victim, the spotless Lamb of God!

3. Yet you, O holy suff'rer, could 'Abba, Father!' cry
   through all your woe abiding in sonship's perfect tie.
   Through suffering made perfect in heav'n our leader now;
   captain of our salvation! With rev'rent hearts we bow.

4. By this you have, Lord Jesus, our hearts' affection gained.
   How can we give you comfort for what you have sustained?
   Entire and full devotion alone can worthy be
   till, love to love responsive, your glorious face we see.

139 The day of resurrection

Words: St John of Damascus
trans. John Mason Neale

Music: *Württemburg Gesangbuch*

ELLACOMBE 76 76 D

1. The day of re-sur-rec-tion! Earth, tell it out a-broad; the pass-o-ver of glad-ness, the pass-o-ver of God! From death to life e-ter-nal, from earth un-to the sky, our Christ hath brought us o-ver with hymns of vic-to-ry.

2. Our hearts be pure from evil, that we may see aright
the Lord in rays eternal of resurrection-light;
and list'ning to his accents, may hear so calm and plain
his own 'All hail' and, hearing, may raise the victor strain.

3. Now let the heav'ns be joyful, and earth her song begin,
the round world keep high triumph, and all that is therein;
let all things, seen and unseen, their notes of gladness blend,
for Christ the Lord hath risen, our joy that hath no end.

140 The head that once was crowned with thorns

Words: Thomas Kelly

Music: Jeremiah Clarke

2. The highest place that heav'n affords
   is his, is his by right.
   The King of kings and Lord of lords,
   and heav'n's eternal light.

3. The joy of all who dwell above,
   the joy of all below,
   to whom he manifests his love,
   and grants his name to know.

4. To them the cross, with all its shame,
   with all its grace is giv'n;
   their name an everlasting name,
   their joy the joy of heav'n.

5. They suffer with their Lord below,
   they reign with him above,
   their profit and their joy to know
   the myst'ry of his love.

6. The cross he bore is life and health,
   though shame and death to him;
   his people's hope, his people's wealth,
   their everlasting theme.

nly power that cleanses me

Susie Hare

1. The on - ly pow'r that clean - ses me is in the blood of
(2.) on - ly love that sets me free is in the heart of
(3.) ne - ver cease to be a - mazed that he should love so

Je - sus, and as I look to Cal - va - ry, his
Je - sus; a heart so full of ten - der - ness and
dear - ly, a child of such un - worth - i - ness, a

sac - ri - fice I see.
faith - ful - ness to me.
sin - ner such as me.

Chorus

And a - ny-thing that

I might give would al - ways be too small to

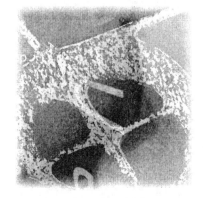

142 The price is paid

Words and Music: Graham Kendrick

ev - 'ry part, I live to thank you for the price you paid.

To verses

2. The price is

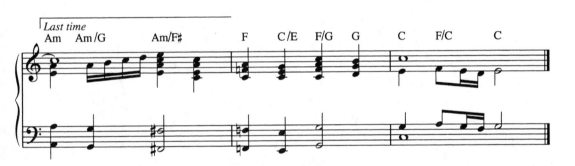

Last time

2. The price is paid,
   see Satan flee away;
   for Jesus crucified
   destroys his pow'r.
   No more to pay,
   let accusation cease,
   in Christ there is
   no condemnation now.

3. The price is paid
   and by that scourging cruel
   he took our sicknesses
   as if his own.
   And by his wounds
   his body broken there,
   his healing touch
   may now by faith be known.

4. The price is paid,
   'Worthy the Lamb!' we cry,
   eternity shall never
   cease his praise.
   The church of Christ
   shall rule upon the earth,
   in Jesus' name
   we have authority.

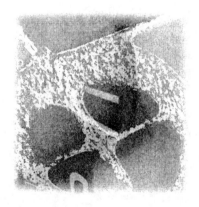

143 Therefore we lift our hearts in praise

Words and Music: Unknown

Version 1

1. There - fore we lift our hearts in praise, sing to the
liv - ing God who saves, for grace poured out for
you and me. me.

Alternative harmonisation ad lib.

2. There for ev-'ry-one to see, there on the hill at Cal-va-ry,
Je - sus died for you and me.

144 There is a fountain filled with blood

Words: William Cowper

Music: Traditional melody

2. The dying thief rejoiced to see
   that fountain in his day;
   and there may I, though vile as he,
   wash all my sins away.

3. I do believe, I will believe,
   that Jesus died for me!
   That on the cross he shed his blood,
   from sin to set me free.

4. Dear dying Lamb! Thy precious blood
   shall never lose its pow'r,
   till all the ransomed church of God
   be saved to sin no more.

5. E'er since by faith I saw the stream
   thy flowing wounds supply,
   redeeming love has been my theme,
   and shall be till I die.

145 There is a green hill far away

Words: Cecil Frances Alexander

Music: William Horsley

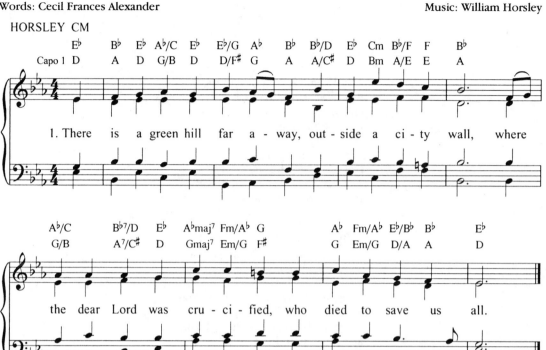

HORSLEY CM

1. There is a green hill far away, out-side a ci-ty wall, where the dear Lord was cru-ci-fied, who died to save us all.

2. We may not know, we cannot tell,
   what pains he had to bear,
   but we believe it was for us
   he hung and suffered there.

3. He died that we might be forgiv'n,
   he died to make us good;
   that we might go at last to heav'n,
   saved by his precious blood.

4. There was no other good enough
   to pay the price of sin;
   he only could unlock the gate
   of heav'n, and let us in.

5. O, dearly, dearly has he loved,
   and we must love him too,
   and trust in his redeeming blood,
   and try his works to do.

146 There is a Redeemer

Words and Music: Melody Green

2. Jesus, my Redeemer,
   Name above all names,
   precious Lamb of God, Messiah,
   O for sinners slain.

3. When I stand in glory,
   I will see his face.
   And there I'll serve my King for ever,
   in that Holy Place.

147 There is freedom at the cross
(You bought me freedom)

Words and Music: David Jones

1. There is free-dom at the cross, end-less hope for all of us,
2. There is mer-cy at the cross, we were bro-ken, dead and lost

the price was paid now we can all go free.
but you've res-cued me, I've been re-deemed.

No great-er love was e - ver shown, you were bro-ken, I am whole.
I did not de-serve this grace, out of love you free - ly gave

I can't be-lieve what you have done for me.
life to ran-som me, now I'm saved.

King of hea-

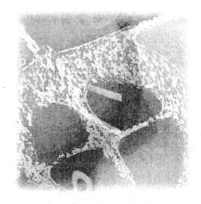

148 There, on a cruel cross

Words and Music: Capt. Alan Price, CA

1. There, on a cru-el cross, for all to see;
killed like a cri-mi-nal, how could it be? That
Je-sus bore such pain and shame, mocked by those who on-ly came to
stand and watch, yet still not see what God was do-ing then, for you and
me.   Lord,

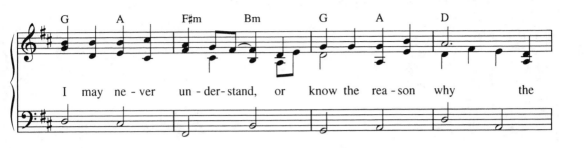

I may ne-ver un-der-stand, or know the rea-son why the

on-ly way to be for-giv'n was that you should die;

I wor-ship you; I fol-low you;

I live for you; I trust in you.

2. There, on a cruel cross, so painfully;
   killed like a criminal, yet willingly.
   Lord Jesus bore such pain and shame,
   for that is why he really came;
   the greatest act of history,
   what God was doing then,
   for you and me.

149 The strife is o'er, the battle done

Words: Latin hymn
trans. Francis Pott

Music: Giovanni Pierluigi da Palestrina
adapted by William Henry Monk

VICTORY 888 with Alleluia

1. The strife is o'er, the bat - tle done; now is the Vic - tor's tri - umph

won;　O let the song　of　praise　be sung:　Al - le - lu - ia.

2. Death's mightiest pow'rs have done their worst,
   and Jesus hath his foes dispersed;
   let shouts of praise and joy outburst:
   Alleluia.

3. On the third morn he rose again
   glorious in majesty to reign;
   O let us swell the joyful strain;
   Alleluia.

4. Lord, by the stripes which wounded thee
   from death's dread sting thy servants free,
   that we may live, and sing to thee:
   Alleluia.

150 The women went to Jesus' tomb

Words and Music: Paul Field

(Roll the stone away)

2. They found that Jesus was alive,
   and still he lives today,
   for God has raised him from the dead,
   and rolled the stone away.

3. Don't let your heart be like a tomb,
   empty, dark and grey.
   Trust in Jesus, he's the rock
   to roll your stone away.

Chorus after v.3
Roll the stone, roll the stone,
roll the stone away.
Trust in Jesus, he's the rock
to roll your stone away.
Trust in Jesus, he's the rock
to roll your stone away.

151 The Word made flesh

(We await a Saviour from heaven)

Words and Music: Wes Sutton

1. The Word made flesh, full of truth and grace, the light of men, God in-car-nate came. He lived, he loved, a ser-vant hum-ble, meek, and in his voice we hear the Fa-ther speak.

Chorus

We a-wait a Sa-viour from hea-

- ven, and he will sure - ly come, in his
glo - ry and with the an - gels and the pow - er of his throne.
The Christ from hea - ven re - turn - ing, his
pro - mise to ful - fil be - fore the splen - dour of his pre -
- sence, let the earth be still.

2. Such hate, such scorn, and a traitor's kiss
   led to the cross for such a world as this.
   The death he died, the grave in which he laid
   could not hold him; to life again he came.

3. Now death destroyed, the grave left open wide,
   our Saviour reigns at the Father's side.
   Where death your sting, where your pow'r, O grave?
   The Son of God prepares to come again.

152 Thine be the glory

Words: Edmond Louis Budry
trans. Richard Birch Hoyle

Music: George Frideric Handel

MACCABAEUS 10 11 11 11 and Refrain

Harmony

1. Thine be the glo - ry, ri - sen, con-qu'ring Son,

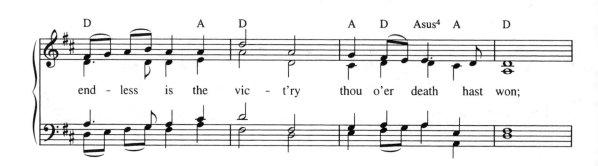

end - less is the vic - t'ry thou o'er death hast won;

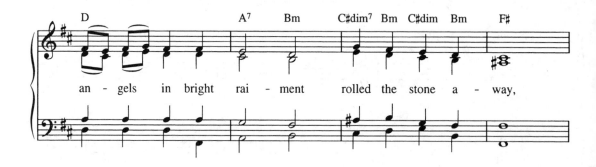

an - gels in bright rai - ment rolled the stone a - way,

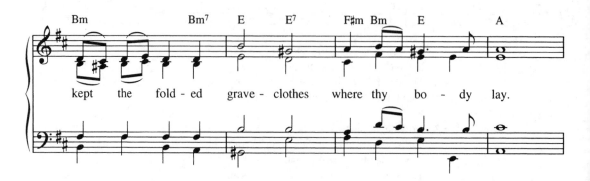

kept the fold - ed grave - clothes where thy bo - dy lay.

Thine be the glo - ry, ri - sen, con-qu'ring Son,

end - less is the vic - t'ry thou o'er death hast won.

2. Lo! Jesus meets us, risen from the tomb;
   lovingly he greets us, scatters fear and gloom.
   Let the church with gladness hymns of triumph sing,
   for her Lord now liveth; death hast lost its sting.

3. No more we doubt thee, glorious Prince of Life;
   life is naught without thee: aid us in our strife.
   Make us more than conqu'rors through thy deathless love;
   bring us safe through Jordan to thy home above.

153 This grace is mine *(The power and the glory)*

Words and Music: Geoff Bullock

1. This grace is mine, this glo-ry, earth-bound hea-ven sent
this plan di-vine, this life, this light that breaks my night,
the Spi-rit of God hea-ven falls like a dove to my heart.

To verse 2

Chorus

The pow-er and the glo-ry of your name.

2. This love is mine, so undeserved, this glorious name,
   this Son, this God, this life, this death, this vict'ry won,
   forgiveness has flowed and this grace that is mine finds my heart.

3. This life is mine, so perfect and so pure, this God in me,
   this glorious hope from earth to heaven, death to life,
   this future assured and secured by this love in my heart.

154 This is my beloved Son

(That the Lamb who was slain)

Words and Music: Graham Kendrick

garlanded with joy, come worship at his feet. That the Lamb who was slain might receive the reward, might receive the reward of his suffering.

2. Look, the world's great harvest fields
   are ready now
   and Christ commands us: 'Go!'
   Countless souls are dying
   so hopelessly,
   his wondrous love unknown.
   Lord, give us the nations
   for the glory of the King.
   Father, send more lab'rers
   the lost to gather in.

3. Come the day when we will stand
   there face to face,
   what joy will fill his eyes.
   For at last his bride appears
   so beautiful,
   her glory fills the skies.
   Drawn from every nation,
   people, tribe and tongue;
   all creation sings,
   the wedding has begun.

155 This is the message of the cross

Words and Music: Martin Smith

(Message of the cross)

1. This is the mes-sage of the cross,
2. This is the mes-sage of the cross,
3. This is the mes-sage of the cross,

that we can be free, to live in the
that we can be free, to lay all our
that we can be free, to hun-ger for

vic - to - ry and turn from our sin.
bur-dens here, at the foot of the tree.
hea-ven, to hun-ger for thee.

My pre - cious Lord Je - sus,
The cross was the shame of the world,
The cross is such fool - ish - ness

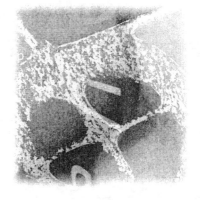

156 This joyful Eastertide

Words: George Ratcliffe Woodward

Music: Traditional Dutch melody
arr. Charles Wood

THIS JOYFUL EASTERTIDE (VREUCHTEN) 67 67 and Refrain

1. This joy-ful Eas-ter-tide, a-way with sin and sor - - row. My love, the Cru-ci-fied, hath sprung to life this mor - row. Had Christ, that once was slain, ne'er burst his three-day pri-son, our faith had been in vain: but

now hath Christ a - ri - sen, a - ri - sen, a - ri - sen, a - ri - - sen.

2. My flesh in hope shall rest,
   and for a season slumber;
   till trump from east to west
   shall wake the dead in number.

3. Death's flood hath lost its chill,
   since Jesus crossed the river:
   lover of souls, from ill
   my passing soul deliver.

157 Through the cross   *(Healing river)*

Words and Music: Mike Burn

1. Through the cross, Je-sus you tri-umphed, by your blood you bought our

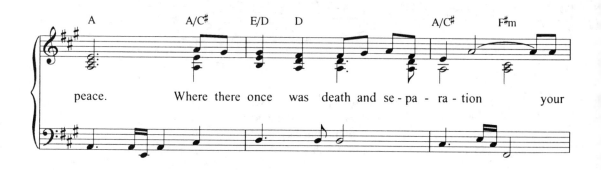

peace. Where there once was death and se-pa-ra-tion your

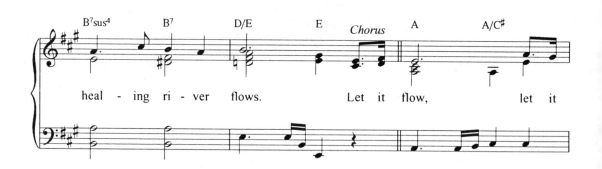

heal - ing ri - ver flows.   *Chorus* Let it flow, let it

flow, let the heal - ing ri - ver flow. Gra-cious

God, we cry to you: let the heal-ing ri - ver flow.

1, 2, 3. / **Last time**

2. Bind up
3. Break down
4. May your

2. Bind up wounds within our homes, Lord,
   reconcile husbands and wives.
   Turn the fathers' hearts towards their children,
   O, let the river flow.

3. Break down walls of isolation,
   rescue those who live in fear.
   May the lonely find love in your fam'ly,
   O, let the river flow.

4. May your church rise up as one now,
   join the streams in one accord.
   Young and old will stand and sing with one voice
   to praise our risen Lord.

158 'Tis finished, the Messiah dies

Words: Charles Wesley

Music: John Kelly
arr. Susie Hare

1. 'Tis fin-ished, the Mes-si-ah dies, cut off for sins, but not his own. Ac-com-plished is the sac-ri-fice, the great re-deem-ing work is done. 'Tis fin-ished, all the debt is paid; jus-tice di-vine is sat-is-fied, the grand and

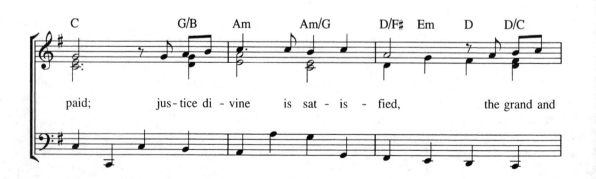

full   a - tone - ment   made,   God   for   a   guil - ty   world   hath   died.

2. The veil is rent, in Christ alone
   the living way to heav'n is seen.
   The middle wall is broken down
   and ev'ryone may enter in.
   The types and figures are fulfilled,
   exacted in the legal pain;
   the precious promises are sealed,
   the spotless Lamb of God is slain.

3. The reign of sin and death is o'er
   and all may live from sin set free.
   Satan hath lost his mortal pow'r,
   'tis swallowed up in victory.
   Saved from the legal curse I am,
   my Saviour hangs on yonder tree;
   see there the meek, expiring Lamb;
   'tis finished! He expires for me.

4. Accepted in the well-beloved
   and clothed in righteousness divine,
   I see the bar to heav'n removed
   and all thy merits, Lord, are mine.
   Death, hell and sin are now subdued,
   all grace is now to sinners giv'n,
   and lo, I plead th' atoning blood
   and in thy right I claim thy heav'n.

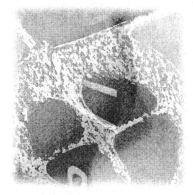

159 To God be the glory

(My tribute)

Words and Music: Andraé Crouch

MY TRIBUTE Irregular

To God be the glo - ry, to God be the glo - ry, to

God be the glo - ry for the things he has done. With his

blood he has saved me; with his pow'r he has raised me. To

God be the glo - ry for the things he has done.

160 To God be the glory!

Text: Frances Jane van Alstyne (Fanny J. Crosby)   Words: William Howard Doane

TO GOD BE THE GLORY 11 11 11 11 and Refrain

1. To God be the glo - ry! great things he hath done; so loved he the world that he gave us his Son; who yield - ed his life an a - tone - ment for sin, and o - pened the life - gate that all may go in. Praise the Lord, praise the Lord! let the earth hear his

voice; praise the Lord, praise the Lord! let the peo - ple re -
joice: O come to the Fa - ther, through Je - sus the
Son, and give him the glo - ry; great things he hath done!

2. O perfect redemption, the purchase of blood!
   to ev'ry believer the promise of God;
   the vilest offender who truly believes
   that moment from Jesus a pardon receives.

3. Great things he hath taught us, great things he hath done,
   and great our rejoicing through Jesus the Son;
   but purer, and higher, and greater will be
   our wonder, our rapture, when Jesus we see.

161 To the cross I come

Words and Music: Jo Puleston

2. To the cross I come, and kneel upon this ground
   where streams of mercy flow.
   To the cross I come, and lay my burdens down
   as love restores my soul.

3. To the cross I come, here to worship you
   and thank you for my life.
   To the cross I come, here to worship you,
   precious Holy Lamb.

162 We believe

Words and Music: Graham Kendrick

2. We believe he sends his Spirit
   on his church with gifts of pow'r.
   God, his word of truth affirming,
   sends us to the nations now.
   He will come again in glory,
   judge the living and the dead.
   Ev'ry knee shall bow before him,
   then must ev'ry tongue confess.

163 We come into your presence *(Father of creation)*

Words and Music: Robert Eastwood

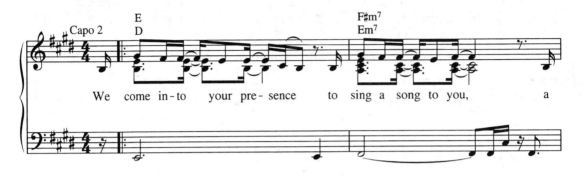

We come in-to your pre-sence to sing a song to you, a

song of praise and hon-our for all the things you've helped us through; you

gave a life worth liv-ing, a life in love with you, and

now I just love giv-ing all my prai-ses back to you. You're the

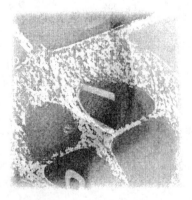

164 We sing the praise of him who died

Words: Thomas Kelly, alt.

Music: Sydney Hugo Nicholson

BOW BRICKHILL LM

1. We sing the praise of him who died, of him who
died up-on the cross; the sin-ner's hope, though
all de-ride, will turn to gain this bit-ter loss.

2. Inscribed upon the cross we see
in shining letters, 'God is love';
he bears our sins upon the tree;
he brings us mercy from above.

3. The cross! it takes our guilt away:
it holds the fainting spirit up;
it cheers with hope the gloomy day,
and sweetens ev'ry bitter cup.

4. It makes the coward spirit brave
to face the darkness of the night;
it takes the terror from the grave,
and gilds the bed of death with light.

5. The balm of life, the cure of woe,
the measure and the pledge of love,
the sinner's refuge here below,
the angels' theme in heav'n above.

165 What can wash away my sin?

(Nothing but the blood)

Words and Music: Robert Lowry
arr. Chris Mitchell

1. What can wash a - way my sin? No - thing but the blood of

Je - sus. What can make me whole a - gain?

No - thing but the blood of Je - sus. O, pre - cious

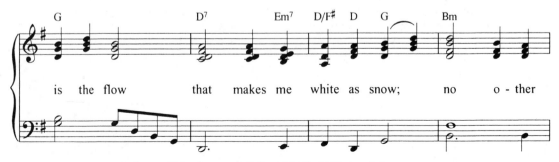

is the flow that makes me white as snow; no o - ther

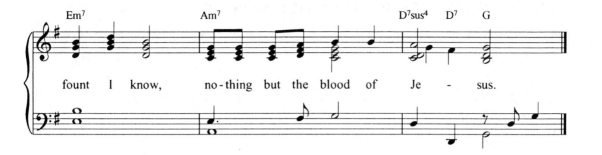

fount I know, no-thing but the blood of Je - sus.

2. For my pardon this I see,
   nothing but the blood of Jesus;
   for my cleansing, this my plea:
   nothing but the blood of Jesus.

3. Nothing can for sin atone,
   nothing but the blood of Jesus;
   naught of good that I have done,
   nothing but the blood of Jesus.

4. This is all my hope and peace,
   nothing but the blood of Jesus;
   this is all my righteousness,
   nothing but the blood of Jesus.

166 What have we to show our Saviour

Words: Elizabeth Cosnett

Music: Cyril Taylor

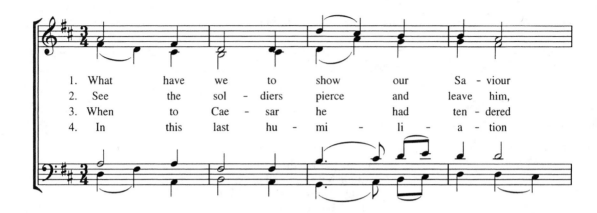

1. What have we to show our Sa - viour
2. See the sol - diers pierce and leave him,
3. When to Cae - sar he had ten - dered
4. In this last hu - mi - li - a - tion

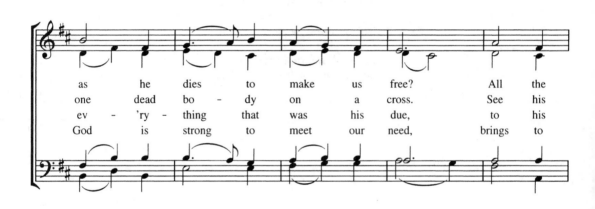

as he dies to make us free? All the
one dead bo - dy on a cross. See his
ev - 'ry - thing that was his due, to his
God is strong to meet our need, brings to

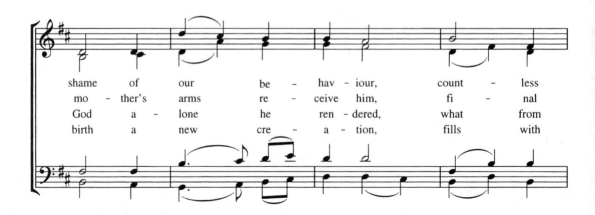

shame of our be - hav - iour, count - less
mo - ther's arms re - ceive him, fi - nal
God a - lone he ren - dered, what from
birth a new cre - a - tion, fills with

years of trea - che - ry. We have bro - ken
fruit of E - den's loss. To what end did
God a - lone he drew. He ac - cep - ted
hope the life we lead. Here the great re -

his com - mand - ment, made his love a
she con - ceive him? Why did an - gels
our con - di - tion, all that hu - man
ta - li - a - tion pro - mised once to

mock - er - y. So we stand be - neath his
hail his birth? Must the friends he loved be -
sin could do: we ac - cept his full sub -
A - dam's seed through di - vine re - nun - ci -

judge - ment, once for all on Cal - va - ry.
lieve him gone for e - ver, earth to earth?
mis - sion, made in faith to One he knew.
a - tion ends in vic - to - ry in - deed.

167 What kind of love is this

Words and Music: Bryn and Sally Haworth

1. What kind of love is this that

gave it-self for me? I

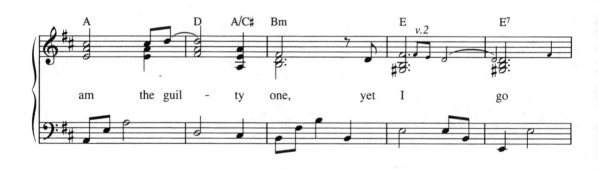

am the guil - ty one, yet I go

free. What kind of love is this,

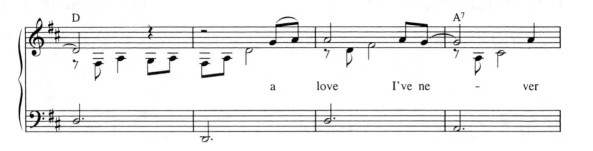

a love I've ne - ver

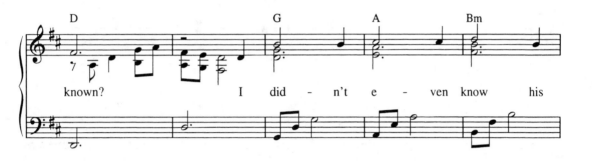

known? I did - n't e - ven know his

name. What kind of love is this?

2. What kind of man is this
   that died in agony?
   He who had done no wrong
   was crucified for me.
   What kind of man is this
   who laid aside his throne,
   that I may know the love of God?
   What kind of man is this?

3. By grace I have been saved;
   it is the gift of God.
   He destined me to be his child,
   such is his love.
   No eye has ever seen,
   no ear has ever heard,
   nor has the heart of man conceived
   what kind of love is this.

168 What love is this?

(I surrender)

Words and Music: Dave Bilbrough

Slow and intense

1. What love is this, that took my place?

In-stead of wrath, you poured your

grace on me. What can I do but sim-ply come and

wor - ship you? I sur - ren - der,

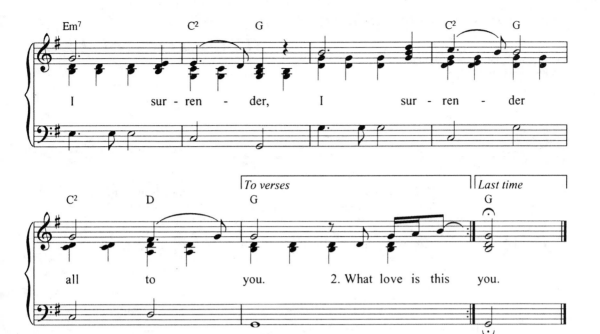

I sur - ren - der, I sur - ren - der all to you. 2. What love is this you.

2. What love is this
   that comes to save?
   Upon the cross
   you bore my guilt and shame.
   To you alone
   I give my heart
   and worship you.

3. A greater love
   no man has seen;
   it breaks sin's pow'r
   and sets this pris'ner free.
   With all I have
   and all I am,
   I worship you.

169 What wondrous love is this

(Upon a cross of shame)

Words and Music: James Wright
arr. Richard Lewis

1. What won-drous love is this from heav'n to earth come
2. What won-drous pow'r is this that held you to the
3. Your blood for e - ver flows, a ne - ver-fail - ing

down, the great-est gift of all was giv - en.
cross, not the a - go - ny of thorns and nails,
stream of for-give - ness, of pow'r and cleans - ing.

The ho - ly Lamb of God was lift - ed up to
but e - ver-last - ing love and waves of ho - ly
And your cross for e - ver stands from age to age the

die that we might have life.

to v.2

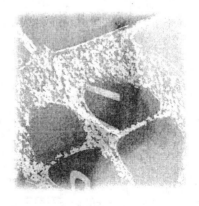

170 When I survey the wondrous cross

Words: Isaac Watts

Music: Tune 1: adapted by Edward Miller
Tune 2: Somerset Folk Song collected by Cecil Sharp
arr. Richard Lloyd

Tune 1: ROCKINGHAM LM

1. When I sur-vey the won-drous cross on which the Prince of Glo-ry died, my rich-est gain I count but loss, and pour con-tempt on all my pride.

Tune 2: O WALY WALY LM

1. When I sur-vey the won-drous cross on which the Prince of Glo-ry died, my rich-est gain I count but loss, and pour con-

2. Forbid it, Lord, that I should boast,
   save in the death of Christ, my God:
   all the vain things that charm me most,
   I sacrifice them to his blood.

3. See from his head, his hands, his feet,
   sorrow and love flow mingling down:
   did e'er such love and sorrow meet,
   or thorns compose so rich a crown?

4. Were the whole realm of nature mine,
   that were an off'ring far too small;
   love so amazing, so divine,
   demands my soul, my life, my all.

171 When I think about the cross

Words and Music: Mark and Helen Johnson
arr. Donald Thomson

Lyrics:

When I think a-bout the cross, when I think of Je - sus,
I'm re - min - ded of his love, love that ne - ver leaves me. Who am
I that he should die, giv - ing life so free - ly? When I think a - bout the cross,
help me to be - lieve it.

172 When the sky turned black
(Good Fri, Good Fri, Good Friday)

Words and Music: Gerry Holmes

2. When his friends all turned and ran away,
   the soldiers nailed his hands and feet.
   On a lonely hill on a lonely day,
   Jesus died for you and me.

2nd Chorus: On a Good Fri, Good Fri, Good Friday. (repeat)

3. When there's hat parades and Easter eggs
   and hot cross buns are in the stores
   we remember Jesus on the cross,
   we remember who he suffered for.

3rd Chorus: Remember Good Fri, Good Fri, Good Friday. (repeat)

173 Who can sound the depths of sorrow

Words and Music: Graham Kendrick

up - on our na - tion, up - on our na - tion have

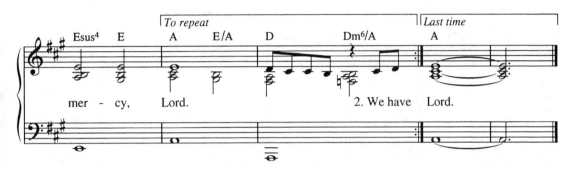

mer - cy, Lord. 2. We have Lord.

2. We have scorned the truth you gave us,
   we have bowed to other lords.
   We have sacrificed the children
   on the altar of our gods.
   O let truth again shine on us,
   let your holy fear descend:
   upon our nation, upon our nation
   have mercy, Lord.

(Men)
3. Who can stand before your anger?
   Who can face your piercing eyes?
   For you love the weak and helpless,
   and you hear the victims' cries.
   (All)
   Yes, you are a God of justice,
   and your judgement surely comes:
   upon our nation, upon our nation
   have mercy, Lord.

(Women)
4. Who will stand against the violence?
   Who will comfort those who mourn?
   In an age of cruel rejection,
   who will build for love a home?
   (All)
   Come and shake us into action,
   come and melt our hearts of stone:
   upon your people, upon your people
   have mercy, Lord.

5. Who can sound the depths of mercy
   in the Father heart of God?
   For there is a Man of sorrows
   who for sinners shed his blood.
   He can heal the wounds of nations,
   he can wash the guilty clean:
   because of Jesus, because of Jesus
   have mercy, Lord.

*Note: some congregations may wish to add to the effectiveness of this song by
transposing the final verse up a semitone, into B♭ major.*

174 Who, for my sake

Words and Music: Susie Hare

O, what grace to me flows so free - ly

down from his throne a - bove;

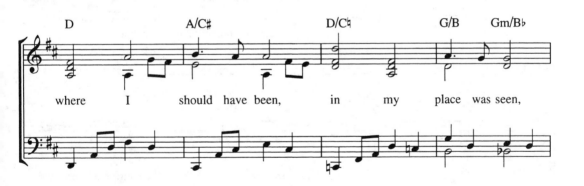

where I should have been, in my place was seen,

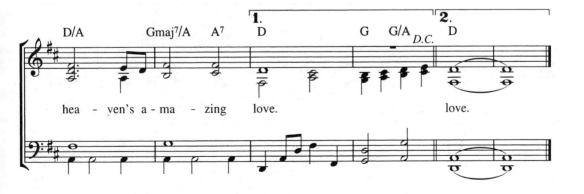

hea - ven's a - ma - zing love. love.

175 Who is there like you

Words and Music: Paul Oakley

176 Who sees it all

Words and Music: Graham Kendrick

3. Who knows the fears that drive a choice,
   unburies pain and gives it voice?
   And who can wash a memory,
   or take the sting of death away?

4. Whose anger burns at what we've done,
   then bears our sin as if his own?
   Who will receive us as we are,
   whose arms are wide and waiting now?

5. Whose broken heart upon a cross
   won freedom, joy and peace for us?
   Whose blood redeems, who ever lives
   and all because of love forgives?

177 Wonderful grace

Words and Music: John Pantry

1. Won-der-ful grace, that gives what I don't de-serve,

pays me what Christ has earned, then lets me go free.

Won-der-ful grace, that gives me the time to change,

wash-es a-way the stains that once co-vered me. And

Chorus

all that I have   I lay at   the feet   of the

won - der - ful   Sa-viour   who loves   me.

Last time

2. Wonderful grace, that held in the face of death,
   breathed in its latest breath forgiveness for me.
   Wonderful love, whose pow'r can break ev'ry chain,
   giving us life again, setting us free.

178 Worthy is the Lamb

Words and Music: Eddie Espinosa

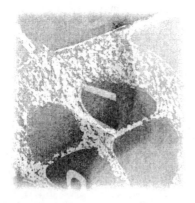

179 Ye choirs of new Jerusalem

Words: *Chorus novæ Jerusalem*
by St Fulbert of Chartres
trans. Robert Campbell

Music: Henry John Gauntlett

ST FULBERT CM

1. Ye choirs of new Je - ru - sa - lem, your sweet - est notes em - ploy, the

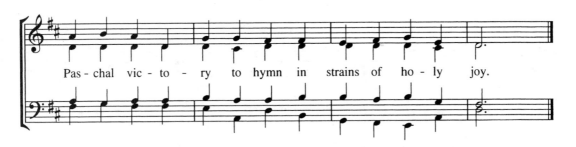

Pas - chal vic - to - ry to hymn in strains of ho - ly joy.

2. For Judah's Lion burst his chains,
   and crushed the serpent's head;
   and brought with him, from death's domain,
   the long-imprisoned dead.

3. From hell's devouring jaws the prey
   alone our leader bore;
   his ransomed hosts pursue their way
   where he hath gone before.

4. Triumphant in his glory now
   his sceptre ruleth all:
   earth, heav'n and hell before him bow
   and at his footstool fall.

5. While joyful thus his praise we sing,
   his mercy we implore,
   into his palace bright to bring,
   and keep us evermore.

6. All glory to the Father be,
   all glory to the Son,
   all glory, Holy Ghost, to thee,
   while endless ages run.

180 You are mighty

Words and Music: Craig Musseau

You are migh - ty, you are ho - ly, you are awe-

- some in your pow - er; you have ri -

- sen, you have con - quered, you have bea-

- ten the pow'r of death.

Hal - le - lu - jah, we will re -

joice; hal - le - lu - jah,

1.

we will re - joice! You are migh -

2.

- joice! You are migh - ty!

181 You are the perfect and righteous God

(I come by the blood)

Words and Music: Steve and Vikki Cook

Verse lyrics:

1. You are the perfect and righteous God whose presence bears no sin; you bid me come to your holy place: how can I enter in when your presence bears no sin? Through him who poured out his life for me, the a-

2. You are the high and exalted King, the One the angels fear; so far above me in ev'ry way. Lord, how can I draw near to the One the angels fear? Through him who laid down his life for me and as-

182 You came from heaven's splendour
(Jesus, almighty Saviour)

Words and Music: James Wright
arr. Richard Lewis

1. You came from hea - ven's splen - dour to earth's hu - ma - ni - ty, heal - ing the bro - ken - heart - ed, sett - ing them free. But for the joy that fol - lowed you gave up ev - 'ry - thing;

2. There in the tomb your bro - ken bo - dy in si - lence lay, but for three days, three nights it did not see de - cay. You had a great - er pur - pose, you had a great - er plan

death on a cur - sed cross that we might have life.
that through the death of one man all might have life.

Chorus

Je - sus, al - migh - ty Sa - viour, you rose up from

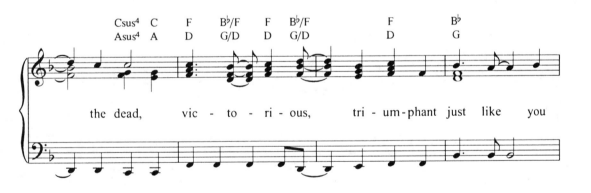

the dead, vic - to - ri - ous, tri - um - phant just like you

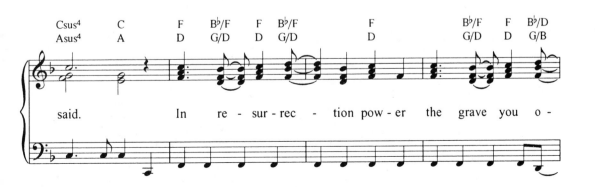

said. In re - sur - rec - tion pow - er the grave you o -

-ver - came   and   now   you   sit   in   hea-ven   for

e - ver - more   to   reign.

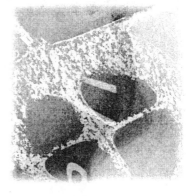

183 You laid aside your majesty
(I really want to worship you, my Lord)

Words and Music: Noel Richards

184 You laid down your majesty

(That's why I give my life)

Words and Music: James Wright
arr. Richard Lewis

1. You laid down your ma-jes-ty to show us your love
love is a mys-te-ry to lay down your life

for hu-ma-ni-ty, to pay the price that I may go free,
for some-one like me, to give me hope and des-ti-ny,

O Lamb of God, my sac-ri-fice. And then you
O Lamb of God, my sac-ri-fice. Now I have

rose up-on the third day con-quer-ing death,
peace deep in my heart, the kind that this world

185 You're the One who flung the stars

Words and Music: Mark Altrogge

1. You're the One who flung the stars a-cross the hea-
whose bleed - ing head was crowned with thorns,

- vens and you are the One who spoke and moun - tains rose
and in my stead you took God's wrath, and died my death

a - bove the foam - ing seas.
that I might live your life.

You're the One who sends the rain and gold - en sun
And as I fix my gaze on you, I'm cap - ti - va-

you   are,   you   are

the One   I   love.   2. You're the One

186 Your only Son

(Lamb of God)

Words and Music: Twila Paris
arr. Chris Mitchell

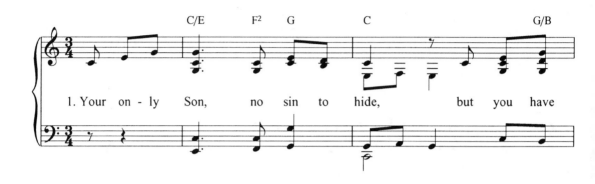

1. Your on-ly Son, no sin to hide, but you have

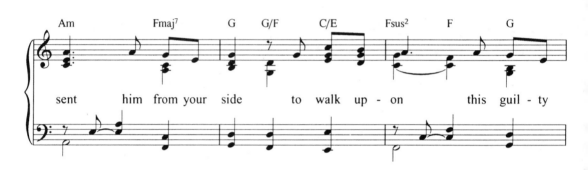

sent him from your side to walk up-on this guil-ty

sod, and to be-come the Lamb of God. O Lamb of

God, sweet Lamb of God; I love the ho-ly Lamb of God. O wash me

in his pre-cious blood. My Je-sus Christ, the Lamb of God.

2. Your gift of love they crucified,
   they laughed and scorned him as he died;
   the humble King they named a fraud,
   and sacrificed the Lamb of God.

3. I was so lost I should have died,
   but you have brought me to your side
   to be led by your staff and rod,
   and to be called a lamb of God.

indexes

Index of Songwriters, Authors, Composers and Arrangers

Scriptural Index

Key Word Index

The key word categories appear alphabetically and are cross-referenced to make it as easy as possible for worship leaders to find songs and hymns suitable for various themes and occasions.

WORSHIP

See **Adoration and Praise**

Index of First Lines and Titles

*This index gives the first line of each hymn. If a hymn is known by an
alternative title, this is also given, but indented and in italics.*

Also available from Kevin Mayhew

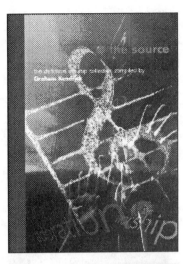

● the source
● the source 2

Compiled by Graham Kendrick

●the source

Full Music	1470104	1 84003 120 4
Guitarists' Edition	1470110	1 84003 287 1

●the source 2

Full Music	1470105	1 84003 724 5
Guitarists' Edition	1470112	1 84003 725 3

●the source combined words

	1470102	1 84003 726 1

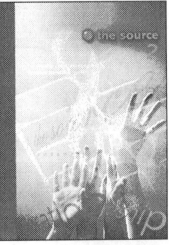

This outstanding collection in 2 volumes of 1099 international hymns and worship songs includes the most popular traditional hymns, the enormous outpouring of worship songs of the last 25 years and much new material destined to become tomorrow's favourites.

A glance at the contents will confirm the generosity, breadth, depth and height ('songs which lift us out of ourselves and fill our vision with the attributes of God') of Graham Kendrick's editorial stewardship.

The books are beautifully and clearly produced and besides the normal indexes there is a substantial Key Word index to make it as easy as possible to find songs and hymns suitable for various themes and occasions.

●the source includes 610 hymns and songs.
●the source 2 has 489.

There is a hardback *Combined Words* edition of all 1099 hymns and songs with Key Word and First Line indexes.

list of contents:
www.kevinmayhew.com/
contents/102.html

●kidsource
●kidsource 2

Compiled by Capt. Alan Price, CA

●kidsource

Full Music	1470154	1 84003 310 X
Words Only	1470151	1 84003 311 8

●kidsource 2

Full Music	1470155	1 84003 845 4

●kidsource combined words

	1470152	1 84003 844 6

Our customers loved ●**kidsource**, our collection of praise and worship songs for children selected by the unique and effervescent Captain Alan Price, so much that we are adding to their joy by publishing its successor, ●**kidsource 2**.

You'll find 806 fabulous songs here by such favourite writers as Doug Horley, Ishmael, Sammy Horner, Richard Hubbard, Paul Field, Ian White and Captain Alan himself. Alongside these are a significant number of contributions from 'adult' praise and worship songwriters.

> ●**kidsource** contains 400 songs.
> ●**kidsource 2** has 406 songs.

All the songs in ●**kidsource** and ●**kidsource 2** are set in keys suitable for young voices; there is a multiplicity of indexes, including a Key Word Cross Reference index, making the selection of songs as straightforward as possible.

The *Combined Words* edition contains the complete words for all 806 hymns and songs in ●**kidsource** and ●**kidsource 2**, in a user-friendly typeface. Casebound.

●christmas source

1470130   1 84003 945 0

Christmas Source is the definitive collection of carols, hymns and songs compiled for the Christmas season.

Alongside well-loved traditional carols are seasonal worship songs, children's songs and even new arrangements of old tunes.

This unique blend of old and new will undoubtedly prove to be an invaluable resource to many.

Christmas Carol Sheet

1470134   1 84003 956 6

A tremendously useful carol sheet, containing the most popular carols and Christmas songs, for use in every kind of situation that involves carol singing.